HOUSE IN THE SUN

Also by Dane Chandos

VILLAGE IN THE SUN

ABBIE

HOUSE IN THE SUN

by Dane Chandos

G. P. PUTNAM'S SONS, NEW YORK

Published on the same day in the Dominion of Canada by Thomas Allen, Ltd., Toronto.

MANUFACTURED IN THE UNITED STATES OF AMERICA

VAN REES PRESS • NEW YORK

For Bill and Stitches

CONTENTS

Part I: Summer	3
Interlude: Pilgrimage	55
Part II: Autumn	67
Interlude: Plume Dance	105
Part III: Winter	117
Interlude: Volcano	169
Part IV: Spring	189

HOUSE IN THE SUN

Part I: SUMMER

1.

I HEARD them coming round the bend of the path. Then they came into sight, the line of burros, stepping delicately under their loads of ore, and the two Indios with their broken huaraches flapping from toes like bundles of bruised cigars and the wide, white trousers flopping.

"Good afternoon," I said, standing aside for them to pass. "Adiós."

"Adiós, good afternoon," said the first man, touching his big flat hat.

"Adiós," said the second man.

They were gone round the corner, silenced in the great silence of the Mexican hills. I heard a stone clack, and that was the last of them. That is Mexico, I thought, the Indio and the burro, appearing out of nowhere and vanishing into nowhere, with no fixed rules or directions, nothing beginning anywhere in particular or stopping anywhere in particular, lost in the prodigious landscapes and the broken hills and the long lilac distances.

This year the rains were plentiful. The mountains all round the lake, and the ribbon of flat land where the village of Ajijic lies between the paws of the mountains and the lake of Chapala, were painted in all the greens there are—metallic greens that should not have existed in nature, like the green of old copper, of verdigris; greens that should only be produced in cooking, like the silky, succulent color of mashed chard; the velvet rustiness of boiled seaweed; vulgar greens in the bluish jade range, right for a dance partner's dress in a honkytonk. From a little way up the hillside, I looked down on this narrow, fertile strip along the lakeshore, where the mountains plunge their feet into foliage —thick green and coral branches of mango, the glossy leaves of citrus orchards, flame-green plumes of banana, ragged fronds of palm, the discreet dull leaves of alligator pear, the feathery boughs of jacaranda and royal ponciana—a verdant sponginess, vivid against the immense blue-silver platter of the lake, and broken only by the white-painted church tower of Ajijic and by the tiled roofs of the one-story adobe houses showing rose-gray and cocoa-pink.

I had come on my walk in order to look for plants of a wild dahlia, small and single and vividly scarlet, which grows lavishly during the rains.

"Those poppies?" Candelaria, my cook, had said when I asked her. "Oh yes, the hills are full of those poppies, if you care for flowers of that style. Why don't we have fine unusual flowers like the Señor Johnson? But you mustn't go into the hills. There are bandits about. You see, maize is dear. Forty-seven centavos a kilo."

Candelaria earns well and hoards her money, which she keeps, I fancy, hidden in crannies of the adobe walls of her house. She is very nervous, and every night her door and window, pad-locked both, are barred and shuttered with heavy mesquite beams.

"Bandits?" I asked. "What makes you think there are bandits?"

"Only last night, when everybody was in the plaza, we heard about them. You should have seen the plaza empty itself. In ten minutes everyone was at home and well shut in."

"And did any bandits appear?"

"Oh no," said Candelaria. "But they say that Venustiano, who has sackfuls of silver pesos buried in his garden, as all the world knows, had a letter from them. So you mustn't go up into the hills. The Señor Professor says he wants tapioca again tonight.

Does he want tapioca every night? I can make many sorts of gruel, both with milk and water, but if he wants tapioca always we must give him tapioca."

She seemed to have answered herself, so I had left it at that, and gone for my walk. I went slowly up a path that snaked round the humps and clefts of the arroyo. Across the lake, the clouds were gathering round the peak of Cerro de García, the tall mountain whose long restful curves dominate the far shores of the lake opposite Ajijic. Sometimes they advanced quickly, tendrils of cotton clambering round a bluff. Sometimes they came sliding round the side of the mountain with the slow certainty of a glacier, all time and the earth before it. Yet, if you looked away, perhaps only for a minute, you would turn to find that a whole spur had vanished, or that a ravine, which had been green and bushy, was now leveled with white vapor. It was just like the Mexican inflation. For years prices had been rising, now creeping and now jumping, until we had reached a plane where everything cost triple. That was why I had become an innkeeper, why my house had a longer terrace, several more rooms, and two bungalows in the corners of the huerta. That was why the huerta now grew more fruit and vegetables than it did flowers. That was why Professor Fountanney's tapioca concerned us, not to mention his punctuality, so that Candelaria went to sleep or to rest clutching a huge red alarm clock, only the hour-hand of which meant anything to her. That was why, in addition to chatterbox Candelaria, Cayetano the mozo, now styling himself major-domo, sniveling Aurora the washerwoman, and aquiline, tobacco-brown Nieves the housemaid, I was also employing Obdulia, a pudding-faced girl recommended to me as "donkey but honest"; Lola, a plump and earthy woman who was a great worker and a great belcher; and Silvanito, a boy of fifteen, whom I had known since he was struggling with pothooks. And that was why, whenever a launch was heard coming down the lake, Cayetano rushed down to the beach to see if it were bringing guests for my inn.

"For," said Cayetano, "if I were not there, somebody else

would tell the señores about the posada, and if he did not get a tip from them, then he might ask us for one, or at the worst me, and that would not be good."

In these years Ajijic, and indeed the whole coast from Chapala to Jocotepec, had changed. A lot of land along the lakeshore had been bought away from the Indios by city Mexicans and foreigners. Down at El Chante, a hamlet close to Jocotepec long noted for its thieving and murderous inhabitants, there had sprung up a colony of week-end houses for the rich of Guadalajara. In Chapala, more houses had been built and were building, more and more foreigners arrived. Most of them were artists.

"Wherever I look," said one elderly lady artist, who spent her time looking everywhere, "I see a smudge of young American painters. I can't understand their pictures. I like Rembrandt and Maxfield Parrish."

The colony, however, revolved in a little group, criticizing, praising, helping, backbiting, backscratching, hating, and loving one another, all agreed on the desirability of living in Mexico, while avoiding acquaintance with Mexicans, and viewing Indios as a frieze of often paintable figures. Sometimes they would come to Ajijic in a bunch, and for the space of their visit the house took on an alien atmosphere. It was as though it ceased to be a house and became a theater set. The Mexican spirit retreated, leaving the shell of Mexico as a stage for these strange actors. Yet, though the rowdier among them are lowering the prestige of the foreigner, their way of living, detached from their surroundings, makes them on the whole irrelevant to the Mexican scene.

In Ajijic itself a number of houses had been sold and furbished up by their new owners, mostly as week-end places. Several new ones had risen along the shore. A Mexican colonel had whipped up a pastry-cook villa in no time, his materials roaring down amid a bustle of efficiency in five-ton trucks. An Englishman had built a long, low house fronted by a superb garden, which blazed with color the year round. The village had become much more prosperous, a spending ground for money earned elsewhere. Prosperity was reflected in plastered, whitewashed houses, shoes, sweaters, and a distressing tendency among the boys of the village to give up their becoming wide sombreros in favor of silly little straw billycocks. Doña Arcelia of the corner shop had become ampler than ever, and it seemed to me that there were several more gold teeth in the family. Javier, her son, once the village's most elegant youth, had an expanding waistline and puffy cheeks. Even Doña Florencia, who had an independent income and no trade, and so could not have profited by the foreigners, had perked up and looked as if she were sharing in the bonanza. But from where I sat, up in the hills, nothing seemed to have changed. The new roofs already belonged to the landscape, absorbed like everything else into the changeless earth of Mexico.

Silently on bare feet and pads, a very small boy and a very big dog came round the rock above me. The dog had a can and an empty bag strapped to his back. I knew the boy, whose father had done odd jobs for me.

"Good afternoon, Umberto."

"Sí," said the boy in a high, shy whisper.

"Back from taking your father's dinner to him?"

"Sí," said the boy.

"Isn't he afraid of the bandits, or does he feel he has to work his field anyway?"

"Sí," said the boy.

He and the dog padded downward and disappeared round an organ cactus, whose uplifted fingers cut the view of the beach into sections. Through my binoculars I could see the wineglass willows and beneath them Mrs. Fountanney, who always took a walk at this hour of the afternoon, standing aside as the flock of beige goats went by and holding her sunshade at the ready in case they attacked. Thin and intelligent, with eyebrows set very high above tortoise lids, she had a look of bored alertness. She wore the university stamp of both the Cambridges, where her husband had lectured, but she was not unworldly and dealt with everything in a competent, unfussy way. I felt sure that, should a goat attack, she would know just how to prod it to the most advantage.

Another burro came down the mountain path with an elderly man whom I didn't know beside it. The burro was laden with great sheaves of wild tuberoses. The man took off his hat as he returned my greeting.

"What lovely flowers," I said. "Are you selling them?"

"Yes, how not. Don't you want to buy some?"

"Yes, I'd like to. But if I carry them, they'll wilt in my hand."

"I would take them to your house."

I hesitated. Perhaps the man would take my money and leave no flowers.

"I know where you live," he said reassuringly. "In that house down there."

"How d'you know that?"

"Oh, everyone knows it. Everyone knows that it is a hotel of the most modern, with little sprinklers of hot water and tubs to sit in."

The scent of the tuberoses, less strong than that of the cultivated variety, breathed up at me from the packed, pink-white blossoms. I told the man to leave me a peso's worth.

"That won't be many," he said.

"What? Not for wild flowers?"

"See how dear everything has put itself."

I gave him two pesos and told him he had a nice occupation.

"I? I'm a charcoal burner. But I can't burn charcoal during the season of the waters, so I work my field and bring in little flowers of these. Do you like fungus? I know that foreigners like fungus, and in the morning early, as I go up the hill, I see much fungus. I could take my little boy and send funguses down to you."

I said I liked funguses very much and would buy them daily, for here the mushroom season is very short and you must take advantage of it.

"Without fail you shall have many funguses tomorrow, and the tuberoses I deliver now."

I hadn't seen a single dahlia, except one perched on an almost inaccessible slope, and I was feeling lazy. I strolled up a little way, round a bend and along a level stretch of path that led to the old mine, started, they say, thirty years ago by Cornishmen, who also first piped down the drinking water to Ajijic. It is quite an elaborate honeycomb of galleries and produces more silver than gold. Every now and again somebody starts working it, but they never seem to be able to make it pay. Actually there is gold everywhere around here, in the earth, the rocks, the sand, the lake water, and there have been many unprofitable attempts to extract it. But one old Indio in the village makes a small but steady profit washing for gold by hand. I had heard that now a new optimist was working the mine. He was sitting in the entrance, a big bull-necked man with a merry eye, eating a papaya and reading an Agatha Christie in Spanish. He said good afternoon and offered me a slice of papaya skewered on the blade of his hunting knife. I asked if he were enjoying his book.

"It doesn't draw my attention," he said, shrugging. "I prefer this."

From his coat pocket he produced a small volume. It was the *Conde Lucanor* by the Infante Don Juan Manuel, a fourteenth-century Spanish classic. There are no fixed rules, I thought, looking at his rough appearance and listening as he talked about Juan Manuel and Santillana and the Archpriest of Hita.

I finished my papaya and told him what Candelaria had said about bandits.

"Bandits? Of course there aren't any bandits," he said. "You know, in the days of the Cristeros I lost some cattle in the hills near my home. Nobody would go to look for them. They were afraid of meeting the Cristeros. So I went myself. I met the Cristeros all right, and they helped me round up the cattle."

He opened his mouth onto a wide flash of gold teeth and roared with laughter.

"And how are you doing here?" I asked.

"Regular," he said. "Not well or badly. And it's a nice place to be."

He waved a papaya rind over the vast view, from the twin white towers of Tizapán to the twinkle of villages that rim the lake's western end. With the other hand he was rolling a corn-leaf cigarette.

"And I found these."

He pointed to a ledge of rock on which stood a row of pre-Conquest idols, none of them remarkable but several in good condition. I asked if he would sell them.

"How not," he said, and we had a little polite bargaining.

"I will let you have all but this green one for ten pesos."

"All right. But that is the one I like best."

"That I give you," he said, and with one big puff consumed half his flimsy cigarette.

I told him I had come out looking for dahlias.

"And instead of a plant, you have some little images."

"And a slice of papaya and a page of Juan Manuel."

He flashed the gold teeth again.

"And I have ten pesos and an agreeable visit," he said. "Whatever one looks for, one finds something else. Isn't it always so?"

I said good-by, and he picked up his book. I walked slowly back the way I had come, not bothering to look for dahlias any more. Clippety-clop came the train of burros and the two Indios returning to the mine for another load of ore. The path ran down into the shadows of the mangoes round the spring called the Eye of Water, and there I met Chui, who is both a milkman and a haircutter.

"You have visitors," he told me.

Merced the mason was sitting on the sidewalk at the corner of the plaza.

"There have arrived at your house many people," he said. "A big family."

It was Tiburcia the wisewoman next. She had a basketful

of washing on her head, and over her amber-apricot face spread the smile that had entangled many a man.

"Good afternoon, lad," she said, for, though certainly younger than I am, she always calls me lad. "They're asking for you at your house."

Two blocks from my gate Chui's uncle, Venustiano, who is my good friend, was sitting in his doorway, glancing disdainfully at the newspaper, in which he has little faith.

"They say there is a pack of foreigners in your patio. Almost better the bandits all the fools are talking about."

Suddenly little Trini, Aurora's daughter, came running, her face for once tolerably clean, and stammered, "Says Mamma, to tell you that Tesifonte brought a mountain of tuberoses and the Señor of the Oven has arrived."

Then I remembered Mr. Humpel. I had forgotten all about him.

2.

THREE weeks before he had come down the lake by rowboat, sitting stiffly in the stern under a green-lined tussore umbrella. He was hard of hearing and had some respiratory trouble that made him give a little groan with every breath. His groans punctuated his sentences and his silences like a metronome. He spoke English in a curious mixture of German and Spanish idiom.

"Name is Humpel," he said. "Mining engineer, sixty-two

years in Mexico. Eighty-five years old, but still they say, 'Send for Humpel.' "

The little groans were hypnotic. You tended to listen to the punctuation and not to the words.

"I am born on the Heath of Lüneburg. Are you not conform that for Germany the unique hope is to restore the kingdom of Hanover? You are tall enough for the Prussian guard. Is it true that you rent accommodations?"

With groans beating time, we had viewed the available accommodations. At the furthest bungalow he stopped.

"This one I wish, but I cook for myself since I have troubles with my bowels, and I must have a bottle of colded beer nightly at my bed. All I need is a stove for charcoal, such as has any Indio, out here in the veranda."

I said that I didn't think I could make structural alterations for my guests.

"I will it pay, and afterward it can arrange itself as a fixture table. I need too a baker's oven. A small one. I bake my special bread, for my stomach. Today it is very tight. I will pay the oven, too. I am not rich, but I have no heirs. Here is the oven plan."

We had dickered and agreed, and Mr. Humpel had fixed the date of his arrival and left. The simple stove and the oven had been completed. Everything, in fact, was in order, except that I, an absent-minded innkeeper, had forgotten all about Mr. Humpel and gone for a walk.

I hurried on to the house. Mr. Humpel had gone to his bungalow, and Cayetano was going down the huerta lugging three fat bundles strapped into traveling rugs, a cardboard suitcase, and a cage with two parrots in it.

Ten yards from the bungalow I heard the punctuant groans. Mr. Humpel was examining the oven.

"Good day, sir. The oven is three and one-half centimeters longer than drawn, and it is not squared. But this is Mexico, no? And it will serve. I like to put my papagays in that old guava tree, for I wish that they have their freedom."

We arranged various details about Mr. Humpel's service, and I invited him for a drink at sunset. I had decided to ask all new guests to cocktails on their first evening, in order to see whether they wanted to be sociable or preferred to be left alone, and, though I felt that Mr. Humpel had a solitary routine that ticked over according to plan, I did not want to make an exception of him.

But the cocktail hour was not a great success. To begin with, Professor Fountanney did not realize that the groans emanated from Mr. Humpel and was forever looking under his chair or peering into shadowy corners of the terrace.

"My husband is nervous of snakes and things," shouted Mrs. Fountanney to Mr. Humpel and then hurriedly, since this was quite untrue, hissed to her husband, "It's him!"

Mr. Humpel was consciously jovial. He plucked a head of geranium and presented it to Mrs. Fountanney with a low bow. Then he picked another, put it in his buttonhole, and inhaled its perfume with a mighty sniff. He asked the Fountanneys questions about Harvard, interjecting reminiscences of Jena sixty-five years before. Mrs. Fountanney answered him in her cool, cultured voice and laughed at his little jokes. We got through the hour somehow, and then Mr. Humpel went off to make his supper.

We were halfway through our meal when Silvanito brought me a note from him. It said:

> Sir! Would you be so kind to keep in your ice, but in dry angle, my yeast? There are ten (10) grams. Rinds of fruit from the kitchen would pleasure my parrots if not else disposed. Please counsel all that my man parrot, who has the yellow headtop, is angry and attacktive. I thank you.
>
> HEINRICH JOACHIM HUMPEL.
> Ingeniero.

I warned the Fountanneys of the parrot, and afterward the Professor and I went for a little walk down the beach. At the moment he was puzzled by a creature which makes a sharp hissing sound at night, and once his curiosity is aroused he keeps on until he satisfies it. I had been told it was a bird; I had been told it was a cicada; I had been given all sorts of answers. But I had never seen one, and I had given up asking. Sometimes I like to have something left unexplained. Not so the Professor. Every time we heard a hissing, his tall, bent figure darted off in what he fancied was the direction of the sound, playing a flash on trees and bushes and rocks, and once on a sleeping cow, which woke a little and looked up resentfully. Almost always the creature, or another, would then hiss from quite a different point, and the Professor would dart off again. Our walk took some time. He got his feet wet, and when we got home he had to change his shoes.

"I can't find my wife," he said, scratching at the lobe of his ear where the stem of his steel-rimmed glasses always left a little red mark. "Dorothy!" he called. "Do-rothy!"

"Perhaps she's somewhere down the huerta," I suggested.

"But whatever would she be doing down the huerta?" asked the Professor.

"Let's go and see."

We went along the rough paths between my young citrus trees, and then I heard Mrs. Fountanney's voice. She was sitting on Mr. Humpel's veranda, and they were playing poker.

"Really, Dorothy," said the Professor, brushing vexedly at a firefly as it sailed past.

"Oh, dear," said Mrs. Fountanney. "You know, Mr. Chandos, my husband hates me to play cards, especially for money. I won't be long, Logan, but you can see I can't stop right now. I must even up with Mr. Humpel. Look at his chips."

The Professor came away with a bad grace. I went to bed and I don't know how long the poker game went on.

In the morning Nieves said, "You should not buy those little tuberoses of the hill, señor. They don't last anything at all. In my house we have tuberoses of the garden, and I will bring you some as soon as they bloom. Last night the roof leaked in the bedroom on the side of Chapala where nobody is."

Candelaria said, "The little Manuelito, the son of that Tesifonte, and an ugly boy he is, brought funguses, and he said they were a peso the kilo, and there were two kilos, but I told him I had not time to weigh them just then, because a peso seemed to me very dear and I didn't know if you had agreed to that or not, and in any case Manuelito has often climbed the wall and stolen oranges, so I told him to come back later, and I still have the funguses to make soup with milk or a pancake of eggs at midday, and I served them for breakfast fried to the señores, and the Señor Professor ate two platefuls and a half, and here are yours."

Cayetano said, "I was out late on the beach and I saw the Señor of the Oven and the Señora of the Professor playing cards. It gives pleasure when our guests are content."

Obdulia said, "Many years ago, when I was in the hills with the wife of my cousin's uncle, she ate one of those little funguses, and she rolled over and died."

Professor Fountanney said, "Your friend Venustiano told me the hissing was made in the stomach of the creature, whatever it may be, but surely it must echo from the sounding board in the thorax?"

Mr. Humpel said, "The Lady Fountanney is very ready in card play. Yesterday night she won of me seven pesos. She is a dark mare."

3.

I ENJOY my food, but I do not like to cook. I enjoy good wine and would love to spend a year wandering round France, stocking my cellar, but Mexico is a hard-liquor country, imported wines from Chile or Europe are dear, and, apart from one or two drinkable table wines from Baja California, the Mexican wines I have tried savor more of the chemist's laboratory than the vineyard and can be classed with the roughest Algerian vintages. I take a certain pride in running my household efficiently and am fond of my own creature comforts, but when it comes to catering for other people, I slip up. I was not cut out to be an innkeeper.

It all started when a Belgian friend came to stay. She had been in Ajijic for a few weeks and wanted to take a trip with me in the car.

"I'd like to get some of those blue and white sarapes in Zacatecas," she said. "And they say there are still cinnamon bears in the hills above Durango. Have you ever seen a cinnamon bear?"

"No, Françoise," I said, "I haven't. But I've got to finish these two stories—and anyway, I'm broke."

"You? Broke? You ought to be ashamed of yourself. You're lazy. You could make plenty of money right here, by turning your house into an inn."

And since she wanted to stay on quietly in Ajijic for several months, she suggested with superb Gallic tact that I take her as my first paying guest. *Village in the Sun* was not yet finished, and I had long realized that I'd have to do something—perhaps sell my car and buy an old jalopy or mortgage my land until all the citrus trees were producing. But the idea of running an inn did not appeal to me.

"I'd love to have you as a guest, Françoise," I said. "But I wouldn't like my house full of strangers."

"You like people," she said.

"They're my stock in trade."

"Don't try to be cynical. You could charge us twenty pesos a day and do us fairly well. Think of all the odd people who might come. And just think of the copy."

Thus it began. The inn faltered occasionally, but mostly it flourished. I sold my car, but instead of a jalopy I was able to buy a new one. I liked most of the people who came to stay, and it was certainly all a new experience. By the time the Fountanneys arrived for a long visit things looked pretty good; Mr. Humpel said he'd be stopping several months. But we were always prepared for new guests at any time, and Cayetano, always on the alert, kept his white coat handy so that he could put it on before greeting them.

"Hear," he said, darting into my room one morning. "Wouldn't that be a launch?"

We listened, and down the wind came a faint chugging. In a moment Cayetano, pulling on his coat, was bound for the beach.

"Perhaps they are guests," cried Candelaria, "and then what shall I do, pues?"

You can tell those who come from this region by their constant use of the word pues. They say, "Pues no," and "No pues," meaning different qualifications of no, and sometimes they shorten it to pos or lengthen it to puesen. It is able to convey any shade of meaning and is untranslatable.

"It must be already eleven," said Candelaria, "or ten, and I have nothing prepared for many people. Ay, God of my life, I go in a race to my kitchen!"

They were guests. With Cayetano shepherding them they came in from the beach in what seemed an endless stream. There was a youngish couple, and an old lady, and an older lady, and a nurse, and there were graded children whom I could not count since they at once ran in all directions. They were all carrying bundles and bags, and these they put down anywhere so that in no time the terrace looked like a railroad station. Cayetano kept on collecting them, and then one of the old ladies would extract a fiber bag or a carton, upsetting Cayetano's pile, rummage in it, produce a handkerchief or a banana, and wipe a child's nose or feed it the banana, depositing the skin on the nearest ledge. My dogs came running in full cry; both were picked up by the armpits and both screamed. Then all the children screamed. Then the adults screamed at the children. Then the children went on alone.

"Aunt! Granny! Mamma! Papa! Look at the little dogs! I've found a mango! I want a little dog for me! There are parrots down here! Something has stung me! Granny! Aunt! Mamma!"

In a small pause the man said, "Doctor Eloy Téllez Macías, at your orders. My friend Luis González de la Comarca, the architect, told me you have a posada. My wife."

We shook hands.

"I don't know that I've room," I said. "How many children are there?"

"Six," said the doctor.

"No, only five," interrupted his wife. "Don't you remember, we didn't bring Leopoldito? His tonsils are bad," she added to me.

"And my wife's mother and a relative of mine," said the doctor, vaguely indicating the old ladies who as vaguely bowed.

I was aware that Mexicans, used to large families, are also used to crowded bedroom life, so I set out to show the doctor what accommodation we had. Suddenly there was a great commotion, and a small girl came running with a bloodied finger. One of Mr. Humpel's parrots had pecked her. Aunt and Grandmother opened a few bags, doused the finger with mercurochrome, and tied it up in a rag, which the small girl at once pulled off and threw away. We continued our tour.

They liked the second bungalow.

"But it's only got two rooms and four single beds," I said.
"That's all right," said the doctor. "You'll see, we shall fit in."
Afterward I asked Nieves how they did fit in.
"Oh," she said, "each of the ancient ladies has a child in her bed, and the doctor and his señora have a bed, and the other three children sleep in the other bed. They fit very well, pues."
I did not know how to charge four adults and five children occupying two rooms and four beds. Finally the doctor and I agreed that five children equaled four adults, I counted out the nurse in view of the small room space occupied, the doctor assuring me that the nurse would help in the kitchen.
"When can we bathe?" asked the eldest boy.
"Right now," said the doctor. "They have all been talking about nothing but putting themselves into the lake."
"You too, Papa! You come too!" cried several children.
"You see," smiled the doctor, being dragged away, "how can I say that no? Until later, señor."
In a few minutes they were all out on the beach. The doctor was at once jolly and gentle with his children. They splashed and tumbled him in the water. The mother sat on the beach in a flowered housecoat, doing her nails. Under a willow the two old ladies, their black dresses funereal against the gay scene, dug themselves little hollows in the sand, sat down, fixed their gaze on nothing, and remained motionless within a wall of silence. As I stood watching, Silvanito brought me a note.

> Sir! I regret the maiden's peck, but it is not to blame for Gustele, my woman parrot, who was tickled by the maiden and who does not like the tickle. It is the Nature.
>
> HEINRICH JOACHIM HUMPEL.
> Ingeniero.

The Fountanneys had vanished during the hubbub of arrival, but they appeared for lunch at exactly half past one by the Professor's watch. The new guests, all except the older old lady, arrived to eat at half past three. Candelaria was not a whit perturbed, and they found no fault with the meal, which must have been toasting and simmering for a couple of hours.

"It's so nice," said the doctor's wife, "not to know what I'm going to eat."

The doctor gave her a loving glance and patted her plump hand.

"Chela is very much a worker, and herself revises in the kitchen everything we eat," said the doctor. "I am glad for her to rest."

At a quarter to five the older old lady reached the dining room, and lunch, which had dwindled to two children eating mangoes, started all over again. No, the older old lady never took soup, thank you. She spoke in a gentle, reproachless voice. No, she could not digest rice. Fresh-water fish she did not care for. She dared not touch beef, or pork, or ham, or bacon, or chicken. Nor green vegetables. Perhaps a potato, just a few, not more than four. Salad? No, never. Nor fruit. Finally she had a can of sardines, a plateful of beans, and a pot of tea. She seemed perfectly content and asked if benediction was celebrated every day in the Ajijic church.

"Oh, yes," said Cayetano, "that is, if the padre is not in another village, and then there is benediction there. Here there is benediction every day except those days."

In a day or two we all settled down into a sort of routine. The Fountanneys kept away at the hours when the children flooded the terrace, and the children kept away from Mr. Humpel's parrots. But on one point of national idiosyncrasy there was difficulty.

In Mexico, the natural state of doors is open. You will see houses with not a single door shut. If a door is shut, it means that the room is in use, probably private use. By an extension of this idea, Mexicans seldom lock the doors of toilets or bathrooms. They are afraid of fainting or being overtaken by some accident behind locked doors, and their attitude toward the function of doors enables them to avoid this danger. But the Fountanneys, used to other customs, were forever walking into toilets occupied by some member of the Téllez Macías family. Mrs. Fountanney was the first to adapt herself to foreign customs, but the Professor was slower, and I often met him, red as a tomato, hurriedly closing a door he had opened and which should have been locked.

I think it was this series of gaffes, which so patently called attention to the fact that toilets are used, that persuaded the servants to use theirs. I had built them one, but for the most part they continued to squat down behind a handy coffee bush. But their new practice too brought its disadvantages since, though they used the toilet, they often failed to flush it. This failure is very common all over Mexico, and in Spain, and the toilet of a pretentious café or restaurant is often a sty.

"It's that Candelaria," said Cayetano. "She's always in such a hurry that she never presses the little handle."

"It's that Obdulia," said Nieves. "She's not used to living as we live here."

"It's Aurora," said Lola. "She's afraid of it. She says the sudden rush of water makes her bilious."

"It's all of them," said Candelaria. "But I expect it's all the fault of that Cayetano, as it was when I forgot the irrigation if I did, because he had opened the door when I was there and startled me, and now I put the little bolt, and if I die alone inside there where no one can get at me to save me, you will know, señor, whether it is my fault or not."

4.

THE days were full of cool, rain-washed air, and the nights reeled with great distant flashing storms, and every day by midafternoon lightning flickered and glimmered all round the vast horizon. Every night determined steady rain fell for several hours—good growing rain, not so violent as to wash away the soil from young roots, not so light as to dampen only a thin surface, which would parch in two hours of the morning sun. The days were often clouded, and the lake was a sheen of pewter. There were no spectacular sunsets, but luminous yellows, from white gold to lemon, shone behind the western mountains and painted high lights on the pewter. Most evenings, at sundown, we sat watching on the terrace, and, as it grew dark, the fireflies went busily and erratically about the huerta.

But one night it was still and velvet dark. Only beyond the farthest mountains came an occasional reflection of lightning. I heard my dogs giving a peculiar bark, a sharp sustained staccato. I went out into the blackness of the huerta. They were standing poised at each side of a pile of adobes as if they had something cornered there, and on top of the adobes Minou the kitten, daughter of Mariposa, who belonged to the house where I had lived when I first came to Ajijic, was pawing like an angry horse and growling. In the thick grass my flash picked up a little creature, apparently dead. It had grayish, white-tipped fur, a sharp nose and a long tail. I bent down beside it and touched its body, which was warm. Then suddenly I felt the little beat of its heart. It didn't move, not even when I stroked its head. Its fur felt clean and appetizing, much more so than my dogs' coats although they are groomed every day. I thought what tremendous courage it was showing, lying still, shamming dead while I, a presumably hostile giant, crouched over it. I stroked it again. Then I called off the dogs and carried the cat indoors. By the time I went back the little creature had gone.

"Of course it was a tlacuache," said Cayetano scornfully next morning. "Why didn't you call me to kill it with a stick? They do much damage, they eat the fruit, and one day with another they'll take a chicken. And instead of calling me, you stroked it, which was a very dangerous thing indeed to do, for they lie like that, they make dead, and then they turn round and bite very strongly."

It simply hadn't occurred to me as I stroked the opossum that it might bite me.

"Never mind, Cayetano," I said. "I have now really and truly seen and touched a possum playing possum."

"Sometimes," said Silvanito, "when the little ones are riding on their mother's back, one falls off, and if you catch it quickly, you can bring it up tame."

Cayetano was a study in disapproval, but I told Silvanito to bring me a baby opossum if he found one. I like to have animals about the place. Apart from the hens and pigs, which I have kept since coming to Ajijic, we have had rabbits, a kid, and a small deer. Of my dogs, Tippet, the Dachshund, is now six. She is still sprightly, and her inquisitive German nose is forever poking itself into other people's business. On one occasion, investigating some wires that were no possible concern of hers, she received a nasty electric shock, and, as the result of an encounter with a resentful scorpion, she retains a habit of rolling her lips back from her teeth out of reach of the creature's tail and snorting whenever she meets another of his kind. Cayetano's little Chihuahueño, Motzin, is with us no longer, but he has left a daughter by Tippet, one of a family of three, all of whose little tummies were so fat that they could only lie on their backs in the soap box that was their first home. Two of the puppies we gave away. One bitch we kept, a small brown dumpy creature with the bare excuse for a tail and an inexhaustible capacity for wagging it, eating, and indulging herself with illicit activities of every kind. Within a couple of days of the departure of her brother and sister she satisfied her appetite on the cover of Terry's *Guide to Mexico.*

"Little monkey," said Françoise, whose book it was.

I bought her a fresh copy, but Monkey remained the puppy's name, later shortened to Monk. To translate this into Spanish for the servants was not easy. *El monje,* the literal translation, was received, on account of the sex of the animal, with sheepish grins and horrified giggles. Candelaria at once altered the gender to La Monja. And in the kitchen she has since been known as The Nun.

Apart from the dogs there are Minou and such occasional arrivals as Mr. Humpel's parrots and a tortoise, named, optimistically, Methuselah, which was a present from Aurora and now lives contentedly in the huerta, near the lettuce beds. I am always ready to receive a fresh animal, and the idea of a baby opossum appealed to me. The Professor was the only other person to share my feelings, but then he was intensely interested in everything, apparently, except his own subject, history.

"Nothing really new has happened since the Reformation," he said. "Just variations on a series of themes. A baby opossum now—Tell me, that one you just saw, did you happen to notice its apposable hind toe?"

There is nothing to do in Ajijic, but the Professor managed to keep himself busy all the time. He knew half the village by name, many more than I did, and he knew what they earned, and what they owed, too. Mrs Fountanney went her serene way, writing long letters to her married daughter, working for hours at her embroidery, whose long stitches covered the canvas with bold Florentine designs, and quite often playing poker with Mr. Humpel. Everything went smoothly, and Mr. Humpel told me every day about the state of his bowels. Candelaria, however, was disappointed in our guests. The idea of an inn had excited her, for she likes to be put on her mettle and had looked forward to a life of constant variety. But the Fountanneys, though appreciative of her cooking, did not inspire her, and about every third day the Professor's stomach, which followed his mood, would prevent her from making some succulent dish she was longing to make.

"And the señor of down there," she said, "he of the oven, you do not know what he makes. All the morning he is arranging his meal, and in the time that I could cook for twenty or thirty, and many dishes, or for forty, all he has is a big hunk of pig's meat and many, many potatoes, with the cigar ash that falls in all the time, and some little cucumbers in vinegar. And his bread is not rising. I looked as I passed."

5.

I WAS sitting up on the terrace again one evening after dark, when I suddenly saw a light flickering and flaring along the other side of the dry wall. Voices called, and I shone my flash in their direction.

"Don't be afraid," they shouted.

"Don't go for your gun," said a man.

"We're just your neighbors," said a woman. "We want to ask you a favor!"

I called to them to go round by the gate and come up onto the terrace. After a few minutes there arrived a man in soiled white pajamas supported round his middle by a blood-red sash. Immediately behind him, and apparently urging him forward, was a woman from whose wrist dangled a small, brightly colored string handbag with a long green fiber tassel, and some way behind her trailed a boy of about eight, holding out rigidly in front of him, with both hands, a small flare. By its light I could see that the man had wide bushy eyebrows, which you do not often see on an Indio.

"Guadalupe Paz," he said. "At your orders, señor."

"Your servitor, señor," said the woman.

They both fell silent, so I asked what I could do for them. Guadalupe Paz looked at his wife, who after a pause began to talk, whereupon he interrupted her and went on with the tale himself. They wanted a loan of twenty pesos.

"It's to repay a loan," they said.

"But you shall have it back within a month," said the woman. "Or in thirty days without fail."

"You see," said her husband, "in thirty days we ourselves are to be repaid a loan, and with that, pues, we can pay you with all certainty."

"Tiquico Paz to serve you, señor," said the small boy coming out from behind the pillar and bowing.

"And you know who we are," said Guadalupe Paz, "because I go past your good house every day fishing for little charales with my cast net; and your servants know me."

"And then we should be able to buy our tomato seed," said his wife.

There are a few Indios who sow tomatoes all the year round, but usually, seeing what a high price they fetch during the dry months, they all decide to sow tomatoes early in the rains when they won't have the bother of watering them by hand, and they always think they're going to make their fortunes. Of course, all the crops ripen at about the same time along the lake, the markets in Guadalajara are glutted, and in the end the fruit lies rotting in the fields because the Indios can earn more a day by fishing or by building or by cutting hair than they can by picking their tomatoes and sending them to market.

"Later we're going to sow many other little things as well," said Guadalupe Paz.

"If the season of the waters continues till late," added his wife.

I have often tried to find out what the Indios sow, and in

which season, but except during the rains, when they sow anything they can lay their hands on, there seems to be no fixed rule: they sow what they feel like sowing, when they feel like sowing it. Nor do they seem to have any system of crop rotation. Some time ago I sent some samples of earth from different corners of my huerta and from a piece of land I own down the lake toward San Antonio to be analyzed in Guadalajara, and the report came back that the soil, while rich in calcium and potash, lacked nitrogen. I have often heard old Venustiano say, "Now it's time I sowed some peanuts here, and I shall plow under every few rows. They say it'll give you an extra ear on every plant next time you sow your corn, but I think it's an old woman's tale myself." Now the peanut is a very common crop hereabouts, and it has a particularly high nitrogen content. So perhaps, even unwittingly, the Indios do follow some ancient rhythm of crop rotation. I asked Guadalupe Paz what else he was going to plant this autumn.

"Autumn?" he said. "When would that be, puesen?"

"Well, toward the end of the rains. September through November."

"Ah," said Guadalupe Paz and went into a long trance.

"In October, or later," said his wife, "we cut leaves, the little leaves of maize, and then we have to tie them round the stalks."

"And this has to be done very early in the morning," said Guadalupe Paz, "by a strong harvest moon when the leaves are humid with dew, otherwise the corn will throw itself to lose. And then we sow a few chick peas and the little chilis of Comepán."

"Then there's the bean harvest," said his wife, "and maybe you throw some little wheat of irrigation, and on the day of Saint Andrew you sow your watermelons, though it is better to have sown them much more before."

"And what happens," I asked, "if you are too busy at the fiesta to sow watermelons that day?"

"Then you wait," said Guadalupe Paz firmly. "You wait until the dance passes and do it when you feel better."

I don't always lend the Indios money, and when I do I give them only half the amount they ask for. I gave them ten pesos, which they accepted politely and without comment, fetched the little notebook in which I write down these loans and asked Guadalupe Paz to sign it, offering him my pen. His wife stepped forward.

"Who knows if I can," she said with a little self-conscious giggle. "Wouldn't it be good to do it with a pencil?"

I produced one. She traced her signature very slowly and methodically, and all round it she made a series of flourishes and curlicues, largely obliterating her surname. Then her husband came forward. Rejecting the pencil, he seized my pen, and, instead of the cross that Indios who can't write usually make, he carefully drew the sign of Pisces.

"That," he said haughtily, "is the sign with which I brand my cattle." (I think he owned a donkey.) "I tell you this, señor, that you may know." He turned and addressed Tiquico. "Child, come here!"

Tiquico appeared again from behind the pillar. He advanced to within a few feet of me, thrust out his left hand, nearly hitting me in the face with the flare, and, placing his right on the crown of his sombrero, he knelt and leaned forward until his head almost touched the ground. Then he straightened up, leaving the upturned sombrero in his hand. In its crown nestled two speckled turkey's eggs.

"These," said his mother, "we give you."

"To seal our contract," said Guadalupe Paz. He paused, drew himself up, flung his sarape over his shoulder, and added grandly, "I forgot to tell you, señor, that it is late, very late, in the season of the autumn when you always sow a little extra chili if you haven't sown enough before."

"And of course," said his wife, "you always put a few more tomatoes for the doubts in the Dries."

6.

THE SERVANTS on the whole enjoyed the influx of guests, and Cayetano peppered his talk with references to the Señor Professor, the Señor Doctor, and the Señor Engineer, for in Mexico Engineer is used before surnames just like Doctor or Professor.

"All titled persons," said Cayetano and wore his best shoes constantly.

Candelaria got on with the men, but she thought little of the women guests.

"The señora of the doctor is forever putting herself into my kitchen and into everything, because she says she is very exigent about cleaning, which she calls hygiene and which she says is because of the children. As if one needed children to know about cleaning. Look, señor, at my table, my counter, my stove! Look if you wish, at my floor! And if the rubbish box is full, it is because five times I have told that Cayetano to empty it and he goes on filling his little salters and pepperers for his tables. And what am I to do about the meat, which I was going to stuff with sardines? The more ancient señora has eaten three tins of sardines each day since she came, and it is for you to know if that is well, with sardines at two pesos a tin, and if I use them for the meat what will she do after tomorrow for there are only four tins left?"

I promised to tell the doctor's wife that Candelaria's work was very clean—which it is—and to send for more sardines. Just then there passed through the patio into the huerta a procession of two women and a straggle of children, all bearing pots and plates and a wrapped napkin that obviously held a pile of tortillas.

"Whatever is that?" I asked.

"Oh, they're taking them to Don Amílcar."

"Don Amílcar? But is he down the huerta?"

"Oh, yes."

"But why?"

"You'd better ask that Cayetano. He let him in."

Don Amílcar is one of our butchers, and I could not imagine why he should suddenly want to have a picnic in my huerta. I found Cayetano.

"Pos, it's like this," he said. "You see, Don Amílcar bought some steers recently for slaughter, and he paid a good price for them, and he killed them. We bought meat from all three. And then it resulted that the steers he had bought were stolen ones, and the owner from whom they were stolen went to the police, and the man who stole them and sold them to Don Amílcar has disappeared, and until the whole thing is cleared up by the judge, Don Amílcar, though he has acted without wishing to deceive, is liable to be arrested So he was unable to stay in his own house and had to hide, and here he is hiding."

Cayetano finished with a pleased smile, having explained everything.

"But surely everybody knows he is here," I said, for Don Amílcar's family had brought food without any attempt at concealment, and anyway Ajijic is Ajijic.

"How not," said Cayetano. "It is certain that yes. The soldiers from Chapala came this morning to look for him, and perhaps they knew too, for they looked in many houses but not here, and just now they are bathing right in front of the house."

I went to talk to Don Amílcar, who had established himself with a straw mat and a sarape, in a lean-to beyond the chicken run. He was eating while his family sat round in silence, watching him.

Yes, everything was just as Cayetano had said. He did not wish to molest me in any way, and could stay quietly in the lean-to.

"How long d'you think you'll have to hide?"

"Oh, not for long, señor. In a few days, two or ten, or maybe less, it will be cleared up."

"If they do come looking for you," I said, "I shan't know

you're here. I can't obstruct the law, especially since I'm a foreigner."

"That was why Cayetano did not want me to come to you and ask your permission. In order that you need not know I am here."

He stayed on down in the huerta, which was now aglow with early oranges. The doctor's children picked them, leaving skins and seeds strewn everywhere, in the flowerpots, in chairs, in the toilets. They and their father got tanned, "like redskins," said their mother, who protected her own skin, thickly made up, with a big floppy hat, for in Mexico to be "very white" is a distinction, removing you beyond the suspicion of Indio blood. As for the two old ladies, they remained pasty and passive. The younger old lady always spent the morning pottering on the veranda of their bungalow, wearing a white underbodice and a bright blue petticoat, and when she got around to putting on her dress, she put it on right there on the veranda. The other old lady went to Mass whenever there was Mass to go to and lived on sardines and tea.

Rendel Westcott came back.

He had been a painter for forty years. He had wandered about the world and had a flair for new places. He had been among the first at St. Tropez; long before 1914 he had been in Capri; he had been at Taos in the early days. Later he had come to Chapala, but he also owned an adobe cottage on a small piece of land in Ajijic, where he often came to give parties and to paint. He had changed his style with the times and always managed to hit upon the popular version of each style. The young painters of Chapala, some of whom followed Mondrian and some of whom followed Dali and some of whom secretly followed Westcott himself and some of whom, horrified of following anybody, were determined to be original even if it killed them, said his pictures weren't painted but dished up.

"If only I could put just a little parsley garnishing on that pink horse of his, why, you could eat it," said Nadeen Braze, who wore a tower of red hair and painted her mouth askew, and whose own work would surely have been indigestible. "Yes, eat it," she repeated, draining Rendel's drink.

I think Rendel knew the sort of thing that was said about him and didn't give a damn. His own style, in so far as he had one, imbued everyone and everything with glamour and was as slick as coachwork. He had been very successful, and apart from that, although he talked a lot about the evils of inherited wealth, he enjoyed a considerable income from a nice fat trust fund.

"Of course he's been successful," said one of his friends, who was doing something quite new in pointillist surrealism. "Why, he could put sex into a lima bean."

Rendel is a big burly man of about sixty with the energy of about ten ordinary people, and when he laughs the lake quivers and the mountains shake. He is voraciously sociable and loves to make people talk politics, always telling them how his own political road is a footpath all along the left-hand side of the Roosevelt Highway, though he has confessed to me after a few drinks that he usually votes Republican. He entertains incessantly, that is, any time after noon, when he gets up, but if he wants to go and paint, he just goes and paints, leaving his guests free of the terrace and bar. Each sort of person who visits him dislikes the other sorts and complains that he is unselective. He usually has several people staying in the house, whose surnames one rarely learns, and who blow in and out with the inconsequence of butterflies on the wind. Everything is tremendously casual, and dinner happens anywhere between four in the afternoon and midnight. The Indios understand this much better than a strict routine such as the Fountanneys'.

This time Rendel brought with him a Lady Connemara, daughter of some famous Southern family and widow of some obscure Irish peer. She was fashionably dressed in an unsmart way, overwhelmingly self-assured, obviously well heeled, and, in spite of her unpractical background of magnolias and bogs, she gave one the impression of being anything but feckless. He brought her round to call and gave us a hilarious account of the trip he had made to Guanajuto.

Now Guanajuto is famed for hanging on the sides of a gorge, with streets at the roof level of the houses in the streets below, and also for its mummies, produced by a natural process in a short time after burial. A number of these are on show and many have preserved not only a human aspect but also lifelike articulation of the members.

"The guide opened the mummy's mouth and pulled out her tongue, and she looked exactly like my aunt Bella," boomed Rendel, his last words already foaming with his mirth. And then his laughter, starting somewhere in the upper register and rolling down like waves of the sea, engulfed us all. Sometimes I think one never hears the point of Rendel's stories because he always starts laughing at them himself before they are over. None of the people present knew his aunt Bella, but as Rendel's prodigious laughter rolled and roared, everybody started to laugh too. He gave a terrific burp, slapped his thigh, and laughed all over again from soprano to bass.

"Goodness," he said suddenly, "I've got those people from Guadalajara coming to dinner. I'd quite forgotten, and they must be there by now. Whatever is their name, Denise?"

But Lady Connemara didn't know either, and she and Rendel hurried away. She came to call the next morning, and she asked me what percentage I would give her on any guests she might bring to stay with me. Unhappily we were not able to reach any agreement, and she told everyone she knew to stay in Chapala. Nevertheless, she continued to call. She talked to the Fountanneys, nodded curtly to Mr. Humpel, and took no notice at all of my Mexican guests.

She often came to shop in Ajijic because, she said, it was cheaper than Chapala, and I met her one morning in the main street carrying a cut of liver in one hand and a morocco bag in the other.

"By the way," she drawled, "I have found out that you could get your bottled lemonades for thirteen centavos up at that little shop at the entrance to the village. I suppose you are paying eighteen at Arcelia's since I know you are charging the Fountanneys twenty. It's a little further from you, of course, but think what a saving."

That evening Cayetano came to me and said, "Says Doña Arcelia, that they have told her that the foreign señora, who is at the house of Señor Westcott, and who they say is a condesa or duquesa, is relating everywhere that Doña Arcelia charges you too much for lemonades. And Arcelia says that you know this is not so, for she charges you only sixteen centavos, though it is true that other people pay eighteen. And it gives her much pain in case that you should think she is not fair, and she has just received a big cheese from the señor who sometimes brings cheeses, and it does not shine and is dry and good to grate, and to you it is five pesos a kilo, should you wish to buy."

7.

"OH, it's nothing," said Tranquilino, bending on his oars, looking over his shoulder all the time, and managing the boat so that not a splash of water came into it. "Though who knows if we'll ever get there."

We had set out early with a picnic lunch to row down the lake, to the east of Chapala, where the land falls into the water in steep cliffs. Tranquilino had been trying to get me to do this for a long time, and now that the inn was mildly profitable and seemed to be running smoothly, I decided to take a day off. He said it would take three hours, but a strong east wind had sprung up, and we were waiting in the lee of Scorpion Island until it abated.

The island is little more than a rock, an excursion point from Chapala, but it has a miniature lighthouse on it and a place where you can get refreshments. From Ajijic you can see it, and often, at evening, it stands out smoke black against the plummy purple hills. At other times, by some refraction of light, it appears to float in the air a little way above the surface of the lake. I have never found a scorpion there.

"You see that willow?" shouted Tranquilino against the wind. "My patron has one that weeps. You ought to have one too."

I have known Tranquilino for a long time. He is tall for an Indio, thin and yellow, always very neatly dressed, and his face, which in repose is lantern jawed and melancholy, completely changes shape when he smiles and becomes round and chubby like a china mandarin's. He lives in Chapala, where he has a job as gardener at a house whose owner seldom visits it.

"You can't live on what I pay you, with prices what they are now," said the owner to him. "No, of course not. Well, do what you can to keep the garden in order, and then feel yourself free to take another job, or do anything you like."

Tranquilino owns a small boat, and he earns with that. He gets up before dawn, tidies his own small garden, goes on to his permanent job, usually works there till about eleven, and then for the rest of the day rows visitors about. He is scornful of the motor launches.

"I carry the gasoline in my arms," he says. "Ah, I don't need a coat. Rowing's my coat, to keep me warm. The days when I don't go sweating I can't sleep."

I often take a trip with him, and very pleasant it is, without the noise or smell of a motor. It takes a little longer, of course, but why not? And then the motor launches often break down and in the end the journey takes as long as with Tranquilino's brisk oars.

Today's wind soon died, and we were rowing eastward again. Tranquilino is one of the few Indios I know who take any interest in birds and trees and fishes. He knows the names of all of them.

"Look at that little carp," he said, as a fish leaped out of the lake, flashing a silver-gray arc.

Two turtles pushed up their noses near the boat, a seagull dived with a loud splash on the water, and blue herons flew close above us as if they knew he liked them. There are belted kingfishers all along the shores of the lake, and these fascinate Tranquilino. A little farther on we stopped to watch one. It was hovering, still as a hawk, and then suddenly it swooped, hawklike in speed and swervelessness. It missed, but it had extraordinary flying control and was enchanting to watch.

"He is quick and agile," said Tranquilino. "But he has to work to live. Not like those ducks. They're the lucky ones."

Near us were a couple of hundred of the black mud hens that haunt the lake. They are useless to eat since their flesh has a muddy taste, and though they go far out into the lake to sleep, they spend their days close to the shores and the islands, catching quantities of fish.

"Look how easy it is for them," went on Tranquilino. "They just swim along slowly, and then they see a fish, and they stand on their heads with their tails out of the water, and that's all they have to do to eat. And if there aren't any fish, they eat weed off the rocks. Why didn't God make me like that? Yes, they're the lucky ones."

But his eyes were following the kingfisher. The flapping wings folded, the hover broke, and, sudden as a meteor, he plunged down to make a big splash on the water and soar again with a flash of silver in his beak. Tranquilino would certainly have sooner been a kingfisher than a duck.

We were rowing briskly now, making for the island of Presidio. I looked back. Chapala was gleaming like a plateful of iced white cakes in the sunshine, but all of Ajijic except the top of the church tower was hidden so that you wouldn't have known there was a village under the plumy green. Presidio is a bare and rather grim spot, dominated by the ruined barracks of the prison. It has an air of desolate weariness, as though, the hand of man withdrawn, nature could really do nothing with the place on her own. There was no one on the island, except a fisher family that lives there part of the year, inhabiting a congeries of rough huts.

"We'd better eat here, Tranquilino," I said. "Then we can see what the wind does in the afternoon."

Tranquilino landed the picnic basket.

"I'll go and see if these people haven't got some tortillas for me," he said. "They're nice people. I know them."

He was away a long time, and I sat and watched the lake. Its eastern rim seemed to be sprinkled with islands, plumbago-blue atolls of all sizes. But these are really the headlands of the distant shore, rising above the horizon. Against the sandy-yellow northern cliffs three cormorants flew, black as charcoal. In the calm shallows of a little bay on the island the easy-living mud hens were cruising and eating, and on a rock at the spur of the bay two shiny black ibis were sunning themselves. A bevy of young grebe, too young to have acquired white throats and still all black, came by. They dived in unison, all except the last, which always dived a moment late and in that moment glanced coyly over its shoulder with its scarlet eyes, just like a coquettish girl at a dancing class who, with her thoughts on the audience, draws attention to herself by missing the step.

I was smiling at this performance when suddenly my eye was caught by a flash of color to my left. On a rock, not more than ten feet from me, an extraordinary bird was perched. It was a foot high, and it had a curved, gaudy beak and vivid yellow tufts each side of its head. Subsequently I discovered that it was a tufted puffin, a sea parrot, and what in the world it was doing on the Lake of Chapala I cannot imagine, for it belongs to the islands of the Pacific coast. I have never before or since seen one here. Its expression was hostile, and the baleful gleam in its round eye suggested that its beak might be a nasty weapon. It was regarding me with considerable distaste. We stared at one another for five minutes or more, and then a rattle of small stones announced Tranquilino's return, and the puffin, looking haughtier than ever, very slowly spread its wings and took flight, making straight across the lake into the west as if accustomed to fly any distance over water.

Tranquilino was most disappointed to have missed it, and I

had to describe the bird a dozen times. But it was beyond his ken, and when afterward I told him what it was called and where it lived he said, "What a surprise that parrot of the sea must have had, seeing such a field of water and then its not being the sea after all. Some people say the lake is an eye of the sea, but I always ask, How can that be, when it's sweet water?"

We ate our lunch in a little bay on the island and set off for the mainland. At the time of the War of Liberation the Indios living in the Island of Presidio held out five years against the Spaniards, who had to bring up boats all the way from the Pacific coast to make the final assault. The defenders are said to have emigrated to the village of Mezcala on the mainland, and until recently they bore a bad name. Any man from a neighboring village whose horse strayed across the arroyo that divides the land of his village from that of Mezcala did not, it was said, go to look for it. The Mezcalteca did not like strangers.

"But now they are friendlier," said Tranquilino. "There is nothing of danger."

But it is true that down this way the people are more farouche. No road links Chapala, midway down the lake's north shore, with the railhead of Ocotlán, at its eastern end. Perhaps one day there will be a road, and communications will make their usual magic, opening up the countryside and polishing the inhabitants. We put into one of three little villages along the shore. A large canoa with picturesquely patched lugsails was loading tule, the reed of which nearly all Mexican straw mats are made, which is the pale yellow green of washed primroses. We left our boat on the narrow strip of beach, and before us the village street emptied. All the women who had been about vanished into the houses, dragging the children with them. Dogs, poultry, and one child were all that were left. We greeted a man who was working on the canoa, and he answered surlily without looking up.

"What is this village called?"

Mumble.

"Don't you know what it's called?"
Mumble.
"I can't understand you."
"Who knows what it's called."
It took quite ten minutes to learn that this was Mezcala.
We went away, and when we had drawn a little way out into the lake, inhabitants appeared in the streets again. I think we were wise not to have ventured far up into the village.

By now the wind had freshened, but it was behind us, and we bowled down the lake toward Ajijic. Even so, it took a long time, and it was dark before we got home. Opposite Chapala we ran into a storm; the waves came diagonally, and not all Tranquilino's skill could prevent the bigger ones from splashing into the boat.
"The waves have put themselves very angry," he said. "Look, how high they are, reaching up to tame the winds."
By the time we arrived at Ajijic I was soaked. We put in opposite my house, but the water there was too shallow for even a light boat to come right in. Tranquilino hopped out.
"Climb on my back," he said. "I'll carry you."
"I can wade. I'm wet through already."
"No, no. I said I would take you for a row, and the waters came into the boat and you got wet. It would be too much if you got more wet when I can prevent it. Next time we go out we must say a little prayer the day before, and then the lake will be as silent as a bowl of honey."

8.

AT the door of my room Silvanito was waiting for me, standing stock still. He was holding something in his arms, and as I came into the light, I saw it was a tiny gray-furred animal.

"It's very young," he said. "It must have got lost, and I found it and brought it to you just as you said."

He put it on the ground, and it took one or two steps and then checked, one forepaw held aloft. Tippet came sniffing.

"But that's not a tlacuache," I said, for after all it was a baby opossum I had asked for.

"Oh no," said Silvanito. "That's a badger. I didn't find a tlacuache."

Just then Tippet rolled over on her back and turned melting, maternal eyes on the baby badger. It understood perfectly and immediately nuzzled. There was nothing wrong except that Tippet had no milk. Silvanito pointed this out at once.

"Wouldn't it be good if I fetched some?" he asked.

When he brought it in a saucer, I dipped my finger and coaxed the badger to drink. It took about half the saucerful, then suddenly did a little dance, prancing on its hind legs, and finally tucked itself into a corner between a chair and the wall, curled up and went to sleep. Tippet walked across and curled herself round, and partly on, the little animal and went to sleep too. By this time the moment to say I didn't want a badger had passed.

"You see," said Silvanito, "how easily he tames himself. Should I water the young orange trees in the morning?"

"But you should have done that today."

Silvanito looked at me for a long moment, with the look of a person suddenly called upon to explain some obvious process, such as logic, to somebody who has never heard of it. Then he said, "Yes, I know it, but all this morning I was finding the badger."

On the whole Silvanito works well in the huerta. He has learned about the care of fruit trees, and the yield has improved since he came to work for me. His most valuable achievement has been the virtual extermination of the red-ant population, which in the past I have known strip a tree of its foliage in a single night. I have seen him in the warmest weather, when the ants work after dark, creeping about the huerta in the middle of the night, my second-best flashlight in one hand and a small can of cyanide in the other, trailing the streams of insects along the secret paths among the grasses through which they carry their ill-gotten loot home to the nest. One day he showed me with pride no less than six holes packed tight with ant corpses. I congratulated him.

"Oh yes, señor, this little powder of poison has much force," he said with relish, "since at once they abandon the struggle."

But with strawberries he wasn't a success. It is true that wire-worms got some of them, even when succulent lettuces were sown between each plant to tempt the worms away. But the crop was always suspiciously small, and after two seasons, in spite of tearful protests, I made him dig them up and plant vegetables in their place. With these he has done wonders, and we now have sufficient to keep the whole household supplied. This year he was making a special effort with some tomatoes given me by Cayetano. The latter had rented a field somewhere and had borrowed a corner of the huerta to raise his seedlings. He had hired a peon, put all the best available soil into his beds, and had built an astonishing scarecrow out of a log and a torn paper sack that had contained cement. His seeds had sprouted lavishly, and as, of course, in any case he had oversown, he had many more seedlings than he could use, and there remained enough for Silvanito to plant several rows.

Venustiano, who gets on very well with Silvanito, came to

see me as he often does—whether to discuss gardening matters, local lore, or the works of Karl Marx, which he read during one winter's illness propped up in bed, a scratched pair of antique spectacles perched over his wise old eyes.

He approved of the tomatoes, but he looked at my green vegetables and said, "Seed and work thrown to lose. They'll rot. The cabbage and lettuce will perish in their hearts. I never try to grow anything but root vegetables in the season of the waters. But your chicks will like them. I was reading in the paper the other day that in a country called—Russia would it be?—they have a plan that will make anything grow. But the writer seemed to think that everything would take five years."

9.

I HAD heard the noise of an unusual number of cars and trucks, but it was only when I went down to the beach in the evening that I saw the gypsies. Here they call them Hungarians, and they looked just as gypsies do everywhere. They had two trucks and three cars, all in surprisingly good condition, and they had pitched several tents. There were twenty or so of them in all. The men were in cheap city suits and the women in the traditional full gaudy skirts and handkerchiefs. As soon as they had pitched camp, the women went off round the village telling fortunes and urging all to come to their show in the evening. As everywhere, they have the reputation of being thieves. In most countries gypsies import an exotic, colorful note, making the local population seem drab and lusterless.

But here it was the other way round. It was the gypsies who showed up grubby and tousled and dingy, and beside the Indios they seemed as restless and chattersome as monkeys. Two of the women, middle aged and plain, with big jangling earrings and swinging petticoats, tried to catch the attention of Cayetano, who was working on the beach, and make him talk to them. They spoke in a rapid easy Spanish, with an accent more of Spain than of Mexico. They tried making remarks to him, they tried making remarks about him, and at least once they tried nudging him. But Cayetano wouldn't play. I think he was shy. He made a few monosyllabic answers, and then he just went on digging.

The same evening we had other visitors in the village. I was returning from Chapala, where I had driven the doctor and his wife to call on some friends, for I had a good deal of taxiing to do for autoless guests. Already as we approached Ajijic, our ears were assailed by the strident cacophony of a blaring loud-speaker. The cinema had come to town.

Every two or three weeks a sound truck arrives in the village and makes the day raucous. The performance takes place in a big open patio. Many people take their own chairs, often in advance. I had never been, and this evening had the idea of getting away, for a change, from the dreary routine of daily accounts. Cayetano took an equipal, a small Mexican armchair of wood and leather, and placed it in the middle of the patio, at the right distance from the screen. But when I arrived, some little time after the show was due to begin, the patio was so densely crowded that I had some difficulty in getting to my place, and, once there, it was quite impossible to leave before the end of the show. Not only were the films boring, but it soon became chilly and looked as if it might rain. I should, however, have disturbed half the village had I left, even in one of the short intervals, so I sat it out. But it was my first and last visit.

The operators of these shows must do well. They charge an entrance fee of fifty or seventy-five centavos, have very small overheads, and draw large and certain audiences, whatever they show. Their sound is so efficient that sometimes in bed, a whole block away, I have heard all the dialogue that was going on on the screen.

Since few of the audience can read fast enough, films spoken in English would seem useless. Not at all. Apart from the kind folk who read the subtitles slowly aloud for the benefit of their neighbors, even those who have no idea what is going on enjoy themselves. One very poor English film all about what the London *Times* once termed "revolting tribesmen" on the North-West Frontier of India pleased everybody, and, though its plot remained uncomprehended, loud applause greeted the exploits of the rebels in leaping from high rocks clear into their saddles.

On arriving home from the show, I found Candelaria waiting for me in the zaguán, the arched passage between the street and the patio. She was wringing her hands.

"Ay, señor," she wailed. "The little azaleas! God of my life, those ugly Hungarians! Whatever shall we do? And the little irons of measure!"

It appeared that the gypsies, whose own show could stand no chance against the competition provided by the cinema, had only stayed long enough for everyone to be assembled in the rival patio and had then gone round the village picking up everything they could lay their hands on. From us they had taken every accessible branch of the salmon-colored bougainvillea that hung over the wall, together with the weights of Candelaria's kitchen scales, which she had imprudently left just outside the back door.

"And poor Doña Florencia," said Candelaria, now smiling broadly, "you know, señor, she of the green sunshade, they took all her little reels of string of cotton, pues, and her needles and many vegetables, and from that Bernardina they took a glass jar of much value, or so she says, though I did not see it there this morning when I passed to buy the little squash seeds for the sauce of the Señor Professor and for which I have not yet paid, and that reminds me, señor, that you went out tonight without we made accounts and for that I stayed."

I told Candelaria I didn't feel like doing accounts just then and wandered out into the huerta. The night was black, moonless and starless, but the garden was aglimmer with fireflies, thousands of miniature lights stabbing the darkness with silver. I saw a man climbing over the dry wall. He advanced slowly to where I was standing and took off his hat.

"Good evening, señor," he said. "How are we of accounts?"

It was Guadalupe Paz. So I had not escaped accounts after all.

I said it was the thirtieth day and that I had not forgotten (which was untrue) that he should repay me today.

"How much?" he asked, hoping, no doubt, that my memory had a fault in it somewhere.

"Ten pesos."

He fumbled in his shirt for a moment and pulled out a deflated football in which he rummaged about, presently producing two very grubby five-peso bills, which he handed me.

"D'you always keep your money in a football?"

"That yes, yes, señor," he replied, "for I am chief of the village team and custodian of the balloon. And how should I lose it then, when it is there I keep my centavos?"

10.

DOCTOR Téllez Macías came wading out of the lake, shaking water out of his hair and smiling his genial, kindly smile.

"This afternoon we leave," he said cheerfully. "You see, tomorrow morning my wife's brother-in-law passes through

Guadalajara on his way to Los Angeles by air, and we could talk to him for fifteen minutes at the airport, and when we saw that launch come in, we thought of it, and I talked to the owner, and he is coming to fetch us at four o'clock."

Mexicans, though dilatory and procrastinating, are also the most abrupt people in the world, and I ought not to have been surprised. At noon they will suddenly decide to go away for the week end, do nothing at all about it till eight o'clock, and then suddenly, in a quarter of an hour, pack and set out. But in Ajijic, where so much has to be brought from outside, it is very hard to keep house unless you can calculate some days ahead. The doctor and his wife had been pleasant guests and the children relatively little nuisance, and I did not want to make any unpleasantness. But I realized that in future I should have to arrive at some understanding with my guests about their length of stay.

At half past three the whole family was ready; punctually at four the launch came; and then the older old lady and the younger old lady started unpacking and repacking; the doctor's wife said her hair wasn't dry yet, and the doctor and his children decided to have a last swim, which entailed more unpacking and repacking. Just when it seemed impossible that the family would really leave that day, they all dressed, gathered their things, said charming and polite good-bys to everyone, got quickly into the launch, and set off. The smallest girl called something to me as I stood on the mole.

"She says," shouted the doctor above the launch motor, "when the German sausage dog, the Tippety, has little creatures, she would like to have one."

I waved a promise of yes and returned to the house.

"Do you know," said Candelaria, "that in twenty-nine days the more ancient señora ate one hundred and seventy-four pesos of sardines? For each tin I made a mark here on the plaster, with my thumbnail, and I have just counted them, and I know that I have reason, because the Señor Professor had calculated the same same, as he told me, for he said that six pesos a day for sardines left very little for everything else, and tea, which the more ancient lady always drank, is dear too, and the Señor Professor said you were not a true man of negotiations, though it is not for me to say, but you will know."

11.

DON Bernabé came to see me about some repairs to the chicken house, whose floors had been flooded one night. He is the oldest master mason in Ajijic, a little white-haired man who always carries a blood-red sarape. He has very graceful manners and likes to use dollar words, adding an extra syllable to any that he considers unnecessarily short.

"I much regret, señor," he said, with a wide sweep of his sombrero, "but I shall be unable to attend to your work of constructation at once. It is because of that Lupe, she of the fierce duck."

It appeared that Lupe, who was a woman of property and who was guarded by a large and ferocious goose, was terrified of storms. Many a time she had heard the lightnings hiss as they struck the conductor on the church tower, round whose top they played in the most alarming manner. Her house was four blocks from the church, but the priest had told her that he did not think it was strong enough to stand, should it be struck.

"We have both revised the house, my son and I, and have told Lupe that we opine that it is sound and of the most solid. But she is not content and we have contractated to build a pillar of brick in the center of the room to reinsure the roof. My son,

Merced is to do that, since I am most occupied with the house of Don César."

"What's wrong with that?" I asked, for César is rich and had built an ambitious house with city labor.

"As you know, señor, it is a fine house, with arches and mosaics on the floors. But the architect, a very capacitated man, omitted to put in foundations and the house is sinking, and I am encharged with the reparation. Therefore, you see, that for promptly we are unable to accept your honorable contract."

So that was that, and I should get nothing done until Don César's foundering mansion and Lupe's pillar were arranged. And I wondered when that would be when I heard the next day that Merced had spent a great deal of money on pulque and was now on a bat.

"He is running round the village with his shirt hanging out and without his sarape," said Aurora. "And the little badger has got up the stairs and now he doesn't know how to come down."

I found the badger halfway up the steps to the roof terrace, trying to nerve himself to descend, and just as I arrived he launched himself, rolled in a ball down several steps, checked, tottered, and fell the rest of the way. But he hadn't hurt himself. He was growing fast and spent all day romping with Tippet and then suddenly falling asleep in the most unlikely places. Candelaria shook her head and said it would all end badly when the badger was big enough to find his way to the chicken run.

"Nothing of that," said Lola, lumbering along with her broom dragging behind her. "What we do is always give him much food, very much and very easy to get, and then he won't think about chickens."

That was what we did, and in no time the badger grew noticeably plumper. When he curled up, Tippet would curl up beside him, and through his thick fur the badger's bright little black eyes twinkled at the badger hound's great placid brown ones.

"Yes," said Venustiano, "I remember you told me those

sausage dogs are meant to hunt badgers, and there they are in a wreath together, as peaceful as two old widowers in the sun. But who knows?"

Meanwhile, I was diverted from the badger by a family of rabbits that had established itself in a corner of the huerta, dangerously near the vegetable beds; by a squirrel that was after the chickens' food and made sudden sallies into the chicken run, terrifying the more nervous hens; and by a sudden rise in the price of maize. Eggs, which had sold for six or eight centavos when I first came to Ajijic, had remained steady at around twenty centavos for more than two years, but maize, which together with beans is the mainstay of an Indio's diet, had continued to rise in price. Now, nearing the end of the rains and the new crops still unharvested, last year's stores were running low, and those who still had supplies were cashing in.

"What a barbarity, señor," cried Candelaria. "Now I shall have to feed my hens on pure little scraps of rubbish."

For me it presented a graver problem. Following the lead of corn, meat went up, then fish. I was already charging twenty pesos a day for room and board, and I was only just making ends meet. The dietetic problems of my guests kept me busy enough as it was, without this added complication.

"The tapioca of the Señor Professor," said Candelaria, "has put itself very dear. Why don't we give him rice? And d'you know, señor, that that Don Amílcar has gone home and without a word of thanks. After living in our huerta for more than a month he's gone back to his house, and now he's a butcher again. Imagine, señor, the ingratitude, for I heard that he had killed, but I did not give myself haste to go, because of the jam of quinces that was cooking, and because I was sure he would save for us the best. But he had not, even after living here for much time, and I myself told the soldiers I hadn't seen him though they had not asked if he were here, and we should have had nothing but one steak and some bones and a kilo of soup meat had not Doña Florencia passed me her brains."

12.

WE had another sudden influx of guests at the inn, among them Eliot and Verna, friends of mine who had visited me some years before in Ajijic. They liked the place much better now that there were a number of foreigners here. This is Eliot's second quick trip through Mexico, and he talks like an old hand. If only someone would set up a drug store at every corner and keep all the Mexicans as a sort of decorative background, Eliot would love the country. Verna is still worried because so many things need a lick of paint, but she is pleased with the social progress of the region and feels that now it is only a matter of time for there to be some women's clubs. They had arrived late at night, and hardly were we settled in the patio with drinks and sandwiches when there was a knock at the street door.

"Señor," announced Cayetano. "Says a gentleman that he would like to stay the night. He is carrying two pistols and is a general."

I went to the door myself.

"But señor," said the General when I explained that I was full up, "at the boardinghouse in Chapala the beds are of bamboo, without mattress coverings. I could not sleep."

I told him I had only one small bedroom left and that it was being used as a storage cupboard.

"You are all amiability, señor. My chauffeur shall bring in my things."

He was determined to stay, so I told Cayetano to make up the bed. The room looked very small with the sacks, the empty rum puncheons, the shelves of canned goods, and the old beehive in it. A double line of tiny ants was going and coming between the honey and the window, and I am pretty sure I saw a mouse scutter behind the sacks. But the General seemed not to notice. His chauffeur brought in a big suitcase, and when the General was settled, I told the chauffeur where to go in the village, said good night to them both, and went to rejoin my friends.

"You're very trusting," said Eliot, who has seldom trusted anybody and is a rich man, "leaving him with all those supplies."

"Well, I think it's fun," said Verna, her bright blue eyes gleaming with interest. "I hope we'll meet him in the morning. That's about the only thing we haven't seen in Mexico, a general. Are their generals as ramshackle as everything else?"

The next morning the General was down early. He was wearing a seersucker suit and he carried a big violet silk handkerchief in one hand and a big black cigar in the other. He made a hearty breakfast of cereal, eggs, steak and onions, fish, beans, and bananas. Verna came in, smart and well put together as she always is, even at breakfast, and the General leaped to his feet and kissed her hand when I presented him, running his eye slowly, flatteringly, from her shoes to her face. Verna has a number of personalities, which she uses like gloves, and she slipped on her sophisticated-lady number. In no time the breakfast table was littered with wit and swimming in charm.

Eliot came in. He is by nature genial, and he holds that good temper is good business, but he doesn't really think that anyone or anything outside the United States is worth much, though of course there have been ingenious freaks, like Shakespeare or Venice, and more money should have been put into both. He always carries a thousand-dollar bill in his pocket, which he is ready to invest in anything that strikes him as a good bet. His hunches are almost always sound, though once he found himself landed with a timber concession in a part of Campeche, inaccessible by road, rail, air, or water. I wondered how he would take the General. But the General had summed him up in a twinkling and behaved to him as one man in authority to another slightly superior to himself in rank. Verna changed into her magnate's-wife personality, and Eliot's geniality took the form of asking the General innumerable questions about the Mexican Army. They got on like a house on fire, went everywhere together, agreed that everything should be organized on a bigger scale, and decided to give an enormous, joint cocktail party. I removed fragile objects and wide-branching flowers from the terrace and shut up the dogs and the badger. It was just as well, for Minou the cat, arriving with the calm proprietary air cats have, was seized and forcibly given a mouthful of milk strongly laced with tequila, very properly scratching her tormentors to the bone.

Halfway through the party, a Mrs. Cafferty arrived with a letter of introduction to me from somebody in Guadalajara. She nodded to Eliot and, ignoring the General's offer of his chair, settled herself comfortably next to me.

"Now this is really delightful," she said. "When I travel, I'm not one of those people who likes to see a country through plate glass. I like to plunge in, if you know what I mean, plunge in up to the neck."

She patted her neck, as if to show where, beneath the snoods of fat, it was. Her white hair was regimented; her clothes were pressed to crispness. She and Verna eyed one another critically.

"And here you are in this tiny village, and all Mexican furniture, and how nice that you let your manservant wear that pink satin shirt. I love things authentic."

Just then Lola, who was helping Aurora with the washing, came dragging along to ask me something about starch. She had a big man's sombrero on the back of her head, like a huge halo, and she was sucking a mango. She held it in her fingers and between sucks said what she had to say. She was not being disrespectful. She had on her hat, and she was eating a mango, and she wanted to ask me something, so she went right ahead. Mrs. Cafferty blenched, and right in the middle of a sentence Lola let out a terrific belch. She is undoubtedly one of the most powerful belchers in Mexico.

Mrs. Cafferty continued to be very cordial and when she left said she would write to reserve a room as soon as she was able to come. But she never came.

13.

A FEW nights later we had the biggest storm of the season. It sounded as if several storms were meeting, and at times the lightning was almost continuous. The claps shook the house, and one was so tremendous that the dogs shot under the bed and the badger woke up. Usually the animals take no notice of lightning but are frightened of rockets. In the morning, quite early, Candelaria, Nieves, Cayetano, Aurora, Lola, and Obdulia all came crowding into my room.

"Lupe, she of the fierce duck—" they said in unison, and then stopped.

"Well, what about her?"

"The lightnings—" said Nieves.

"That very big thunder, it must have been—" said Obdulia.

"And she so afraid—" said Aurora.

"The pillar—" said Candelaria but was for once talked down.

"Merced was drunken when he built it—" said Cayetano.

"And they say that her sister Bernardina, she of the little shop, who squints, will inherit all," put in Aurora.

"D'you mean she's dead?" I asked.

"Dead, dead," said Candelaria, talking at a great rate and quelling interruption with a defiant circular glance, "the house was struck, and the pillar crumbled, and everyone came running, but it was hard to get through the rubble, and when they did—it took two hours—they found the pillar had fallen on that beautiful bed of metal with the pink gauze curtains, and on Lupe, and there she was, crushed as if on a grindstone though the duck was not hurt."

I said we must hope at any rate that she was killed outright and did not suffer.

"Yes," said Aurora, "she was dead when we found her, for the soul was already leaving the body. Tiburcia, who lives near by, went and brought a little piece of mirror—a piece of that big one that broke itself here not long ago and Tiburcia took the piece out of the rubbish heap for I saw her—and we held it to Lupe's mouth, and it clouded, so we knew that was the soul departing."

Interlude: PILGRIMAGE

14.

LIGHTNING is with us all the summer. It forks and it shimmers and it zips, and sometimes it pulsates for seconds on end. It is white and yellow and greenish and bluish and carnation pink. It has given rise to legends. They say that, in the seventeenth century, the storms in Guadalajara were so severe that repeatedly bellringers in the churches were killed, so that at last they brought into the city the most venerated virgin of the neighborhood, she of Zapopan, who is one of three similar images brought to Jalisco by the first settlers from Spain. Her sisters are at Talpa and San Juan de los Lagos, and all three wear much wealth in jewels. Ever since that first summer, centuries ago, she has passed the whole rainy season in Guadalajara, from June through September, staying two weeks in each church. Since she began to make her sojourn the storms have never again been so violent, and when, in the first days of October every year, she is taken back to her own shrine outside the city, a great pilgrimage goes with her in thanksgiving.

There is nothing like a pilgrimage for displaying on a small canvas the character of a whole people, and when a Mexican makes a vow he sets about it in his own way. Not for him the crowded pilgrim trains and busy boardinghouses of middle-class Lourdes nor the remote intensity and rain-washed faith of misty Croaghpatrick. His own faith came from sunnier lands, and his romerías recall, rather, the splendid church pageants of Seville, Montserrat, and Loreto, or the autumn pilgrimage to Montevergine when Naples spills its vivid multitudes in murmuring thousands across the corn fields of Campania.

Clearly much of the spirit of the Mexican romería was imported by the conquistadors, yet generations before the days of Cortés Indios were traveling in their thousands from all over Anahuac to the shrine of the air god, Quetzalcoatl, on the summit of his forty-acre pyramid at Cholula, where later the Spaniards installed the Virgen de los Remedios. To this day they answer the clangor of her bells as once they obeyed the summons of the Teponaztli, the sacred drum of ancient Mexico. The change has, perhaps, been less fundamental than Prescott would have us believe, for Remedios too understands warriors and has witnessed the shedding of blood, and, like her rival Guadalupe, patron of the revolution, she held general's rank during the struggle for independence.

Our Lady of Zapopan wears a jeweled sword, for she too is a general, and her progress is as much a triumph as any enjoyed by Caesar or Pompey. Of course, the journey is a matter of only four or five miles, and the ardor and enthusiasm of the crowds are therefore unabated through fatigue or exposure. She is very renowned, for she has often crowned prayer with fulfillment, and this, coupled with her accessibility, has brought her numerous ex-voto pictures, little oil paintings on metal illustrating incidents in which her help was besought or recognized. So many has she received that they are stolen in quantities and sold to those interested in such things. I once saw a suitcase containing hundreds, all from Zapopan, two of which I have before me as I write. One of them depicts a she-ass with the Virgin of Zapopan hovering in one corner and a legend stating that by her aid the animal, which had been lost, was found again. The other shows an improbable green hill over which a man in white pajamas is walking with a leisurely gait, while a yard or two behind him three soldiers are in hot pursuit with red and yellow flames darting from the muzzles of their guns. We are told the man was not hurt!

"In the house of my aunt who lives in Zapopan there are many such pictures," Candelaria told me, "but they do not call my attention. My aunt is pious and rich; I have seen where she hides her centavos under the floor. But I shall not make the struggle this year. You see, when I stay with her I cannot sleep, for, imagine to yourself, señor, though her bed is of the finest iron, little animals attack it all night."

Many Ajijic folk go to Zapopan every year, those who travel afoot or on donkeyback setting out three or four days in advance, for though it is no great distance and the fiesta lasts officially one day only, the whole jaunt takes a week. This year Venustiano had taken a vow to make the pilgrimage, goaded as usual, I think, by his wife. I took Verna round to see him, and we found him in his yard pruning a castor-oil tree so as to let in the sunlight to a small, tired-looking begonia cutting.

"Oh yes, I'm going," he said, swinging his sarape around him with the air of a Roman senator. "They say it's a very fine fiesta, if you care for things of that sort."

Verna is keen on folklore in the same way that she is keen on antiques, lectures, local handicrafts, psychology, and most of those other subjects suitably close to the heart of the average well-to-do New England lady. She fell hard for the idea of attending Our Lady to Zapopan.

"I can't wait to see those quaint old dances and all the cunning costumes," she said. "And I still have a roll of Kodachrome. We could stop over in Guadalajara on our way to the border, Eliot, and then we could all go together. Couldn't we, Eliot?"

I have to go to Guadalajara every week to buy those things for the inn that Ajijic and Chapala do not provide, so it was decided that we meet in the city on the eve of the feast of Zapopan. I made an early start and spent the morning going about my various chores. At a little before two o'clock I called round at the hotel and found Verna and Eliot in the bar, arguing about something, and the air was such that I thought I wouldn't get myself involved.

"Look," I said, "I'm going to the market now. I can't do any more shopping round here because all the shops are closed until four."

"Isn't that crazy!" said Verna. Her fingers were pulling at the big emerald engagement ring on her left hand, and her bright blue eyes snapped critically round the bar, taking everything in.

"No, Verna," I said. "It isn't crazy. The Mexicans like it that way, and what you have just said implies, in a nutshell, why Mexicans fear economic control from the United States. They dread the intrusion into their private life and habits."

"Exactly," said Eliot, chomping on his cigar and not agreeing with me in the very least. "It's all a question of individual liberty, Verna. Free people don't like someone else telling them what they must do, and that is why I won't go all the way to Zapopan on foot."

We went to bed early that night and left word to be called at four o'clock in the morning. At half past, Verna and I met for a thermos of coffee downstairs in the lobby. Eliot had complained of a headache and refused to get up, and from the expression on Verna's face I decided it was prudent to let the subject drop.

Together we went out into the street. All night the crowds had made merry. The bars had been filled till a late hour, and the jingle of music had permeated every quiet plaza and patio in the city. Now began the drift northward, out of town. Up the fashionable Avenida Vallarta the people moved, an endless tide of variegated color in the headlights of a thousand cars, which slowly nosed their way through the press. We joined them at once, for you must go early to see the best of the ceremony.

The Lady herself starts before dawn from the Church of San Felipe, riding in a carriage whose roof is surmounted by a huge crown of fresh flowers. Behind the carriage walk the plumed, caparisoned black horses, for they are never allowed to draw the Lady's coach but are always replaced by pious human muscle. For months now, in church after church throughout the city, she has stood in splendor, stiff and jeweled and adored, a flame of flowers and candles tiered in worship beneath her pedestal. Now she was going home to her white church amid the quiet groves of Zapopan. And she did not go alone. Around her and after her came the pilgrims, and before her they streamed in their thousands down the dark road: poor women muffled in shawls, some praying as they went, some kneeling down every ten paces; rich girls, with hair elaborately arranged under the black chiffon veil, with mother and aunts hovering at their sides to help them over rough places, for they were barefoot, having taken a vow; Indios lying down, rising, lying down again, measuring the whole road out from the city with their bodies; others, half naked, their flesh pierced by cactus thorns.

"They're cuckoo," said Verna.

A well-dressed city boy went by, his face, in the flare of a torch, long and yellow and solemn, out of a Spanish picture, his eyes fixed ahead high up in the darkness and his bare feet bleeding. Then there were the dancers.

All the way down the road the groups were scattered, thirty or forty strong, unearthly under the fire of torches, magic under the rainbow-colored umbrellas of rocket-borne stars, each group in a different fancy dress, each doing a different step, each with its little band of musicians, fiddling, blowing horns and fifes, and drumming out on rattles its sharp, individual rhythm. The firecrackers snapped; the metal disks clattered. Nightmare faces appeared and vanished in the gloom—here, broad, mongoloid features smothered in lipstick and glittering sequins; there, a flour-white vacuous mask, glassy-eyed, whose long black beard rippled over its wearer's gnarled brown chest. All the way, amid gusts of incense and garlic, dancing and prancing, in faith and folly, wondrous and infantile and pathetic; all the way, out from the city to the wide gracious church in its great court among the cypresses; each year the Indios came dancing.

For centuries they have come stamping tum-ta-tóm-tum to a Christian shrine, and nobody knows whether they had been coming year by year long before that, long before the conquest. They were gallant and noble and dedicated, and yet they were a little sickening too, with their dressing up and their ritual air-beating and their glad, profitless penance. And we too walked along with the pilgrims, Verna and I, upheld by no faith, dedicated to no penance, sightseers come to see a show.

"Look," said Verna. "Those are tight already."

The group of dancing Indios, aglitter in the torchlight with murky red and peacock, swayed and tottered as they stamped along, tum-ta-tóm-tum. Their faces were tense black masks, and only out of the shadow between brow and cheekbone there shone wild gleams that were their eyes. Yes, Verna, they are tight. But with what? With drink, or with exhaustion, or with fervor? For months now, in distant villages, they have practiced their steps, and here they are, those with vows to fulfill, and those who have come to buy, and sell, and cheat, and worship, and steal, and get drunk, and whore. A foot-high image, a satin puppet all bediamonded, is a splendid pretext for a binge.

We were now more than halfway to Zapopan, and we climbed the high bank by the roadside to rest a little and watch the crowd go by. Already the eastern sky was smudged with the first streaks of tawny light. Behind us, sleek and green from the rains, calm and empty of people, stretched the most fashionable golf course in western Mexico. Before us, down the road, like a mountain river in spate, foamed and boiled the multitude of pilgrims. As the sun came up, the dark, sweaty Indio faces that had seemed masks became faces again, and the weird dresses—tinsel-banded trousers, shiny robes clasped on one shoulder, tinfoil crowns—seized real colors from the sunrise and stopped being momentary murky glitters. The twin spikes of turquoise light to our left, which had served as a beacon for the last two hours, faded into the ornate and silvery mass of Zapopan's domed and fretted towers.

It was now seven o'clock. Some said the Lady would pass soon after nine. Verna and I walked on into the little town. Here the streets were crammed; the roofs were lined; every window was thickset with people. The crowd became almost impassable for a moment as we turned the last bend into the main street. By the side of the road was a cart that, judging from the leaves around it, had recently been full of sugar cane, and its enterprising owner, his pouch already stuffed with silver pesos, was earning a bonus by turning the empty vehicle into a miniature grandstand. Opposite, a loudspeaker blared out news, instructions, advertisements and rumbas in an unceasing flow. As we moved into the straight avenue that led up to the Lady's church, our footsteps were momentarily deadened. We kicked up some damp sawdust, and there was a smell of disinfectant. In spite of the festivities, the authorities had not neglected the precautions to be taken against the hoof-and-mouth epidemic.

"I suppose they'll make Our Lady get out of her carriage and walk through this," said Verna.

And now we were at the end of our journey. Between ourselves and the massive carved portal milled ten or fifteen thousand people. All the way the road was lined with trophies of giant golden sunflowers bound up with sky-blue and white ribbons, the Lady's colors. On the sidewalk innumerable stall keepers traded in soup, candles, ice cream, balloons, coffee, nuts, colored waters, tortillas, and confetti. Presently I was hailed from a rooftop by some Mexican friends. The door of the house was open, and the people were drifting in and out with the greatest self-possession in order to avail themselves of the drinking fountain, washbasins, and toilet. We went in and, finding a ladder, climbed up to the roof, where we were greeted by a number of kind people we had never seen. Verna fell silent, and we settled down to wait for the coming of the Lady.

From moment to moment the street presented scenes of ever increasing animation. Fresh bands of dancers continually passed. Our host told us there were about sixty groups in all. Now, in daylight, it could be seen that for the most part the costumes followed the traditional patterns of Indio and conquistador, in endless permutations, though here and there was a Roman soldier, and once Verna pointed out a small party of what we took to be imps. Still the crowd came pouring through. Little girls offered us streamers, flowers, and confetti to throw when the procession should arrive. A man with no legs went by, wielding his crutches with the utmost speed and agility, followed by his family of seven children, whose mother carried on her head a basket such as Tippet uses for a bed, in which reposed a mountain of tortillas and a very small baby.

By now the sun stood high and it began to get hot. For a while I found a little shade below one of the outspread branches of a tall araucaria that grew in the patio, but it was not easy to resist the lure of the street, and I was soon back again, sitting on the roof balustrade. Below me was a man in a costume trimmed with hundreds of wooden bobbins. I think he must have been a deserter from a group of dancers, for he was evidently feeling the heat more than his neighbors and had made an improvised parasol out of two sticks of sugar cane and a banana leaf. Behind him came one of the more devoted pilgrims, a darkly clad middle-aged woman progressing very slowly, on her knees. It was clear she had come a long way like this, for she was tired to the point of exhaustion. Her face was gray and furrowed with tears of sheer fatigue, and after every two or three steps she would sit back on her heels and rest. A man held either hand, and friendly bystanders spread blankets and sarapes before her as she shuffled painfully along. Presently she drew abreast of a party of dancers, and from the center of the group darted a cavalier in white and lilac satin with plumed hat and rapier at his hip. With a flamboyant, yet somehow reverent, obeisance he spread his glistening rayon cloak in her path, and in a second I was transported from the sunny dust of Mexico to the cool turf of an English cathedral close, to the climax of a pageant, where as a small boy I had gaped in unstinted admiration as Sir Walter Raleigh tendered his humble duty to Queen Elizabeth.

"Here they come," said Verna, as a series of violent explosions interrupted my thoughts.

Smoke puffs filled the sky around us, and into the main street rode the first of the charros. They came in single file along either side of the street, horsemen of every age, and from every town in the state, their jackets frogged and embroidered, their sombreros laced with silver, whips in hand and lariats at the saddle bow, joking with the crowd and slowly closing their ranks to clear the center of the road for the procession that was to follow. Their horses were plump and glossy: blacks, chestnuts, bays, roans, and skewbalds, with here and there an elegant blond palomino. One or two women rode with the men, dressed mostly in the wide skirt and flower-embroidered blouse of the china poblana costume. They faced inward and dressed their ranks smartly. All the spectators on foot were now excluded from the center of the road, though at one moment, when the mayor's car edged its way through the barrier, it was followed amid shouts of laughter by a ragged urchin who capered gaily up the street, putting out his tongue at the dignified cavaliers to right and left.

Then came the procession. First a company of uniformed women—nurses, perhaps—came marching up the street followed by two bands and cars containing officials. When the bands had passed, we heard the singing, the stately solemn measure sung by the Lady's escort as they bore her through the kneeling crowds up the last slope into the town. Dancers preceded her, and a great company of singing Zapopanos bearing her blue and white flags; and these were followed by a concourse of women carrying baskets of every sort of flower, small bunches and huge trophies alike. Then came the Lady herself. She rode in a modest four-wheeler, but two hundred youths drew her along with ropes of Mexican sisal. The carriage was almost hidden by banks of white flowers—camellias, roses, and gardenias—and a brightly jeweled crown of many-colored flowers adorned the roof. We could hear the clapping and the cheers down the street, and, as the carriage passed, the watchers crossed themselves and bared their heads. And now we had a brief glance through the open window at the Lady herself. She was wearing no high coronet of diamonds, she was encased in no gemmed stomacher, and they had girt her with no jeweled sword. She wore a pilgrim's cloak and a little traveling hat tied beneath the chin with ribbons. So she journeyed home—gray clad among her flowers, drawn by four hundred hands—home to the cool nave between the long columns that were fingers raised, not in admonition, but in triumphant thanksgiving for mercy, majesty, and glory.

"Just a doll," said Verna. "Of course, it's an antique."

Then we saw the American soldier. Among the drab clothes of the pilgrims and the gaudy costumes of the dancers, his uniform was the most exotic fancy dress of all. He stood there staring, and as the Lady went by, he gave her a military salute as if he knew she were a general. Maybe he should have bared his head like the rest. But he didn't. He saluted. Then, as the carriage rolled on and those who had lined the sidewalks swarmed to join the pilgrims, we lost sight of him.

We struggled down into the street. It wasn't easy to get near the courtyard of the church or through the gates in the iron-railed wall. Above the mob, the leaves of the cypresses and eucalyptus trees stirred in a little wind, and the towers of the church were silver filigree against a sky of blue glass. All over the courtyard were groups of dancers, arranged in oblongs, half a group watching while half danced. Individuals who had vowed to dance all day stamped back and forth, stopping sometimes for a glass of lemonade or tequila. Hundreds of rattles banged; the church bells clanged. The dancers melted in their bright costumes, worn over sweatshirts and denim trousers. All to the glory of the Lady, they spun and belched and sweated; they stamped and burped and spat. Through the gates streamed the pilgrims, rich and poor, plenty of them people I knew. I saw the Governor and his staff go by. And then Venustiano came. He came with his free stride, this reader of Carlos Marx, and at the gate he knelt down, for that was the vow he had made, to go on his knees from the gates to the church doors. Even on his knees he did not look humble, and his wrinkled face gave no window to his thoughts. I looked at the turquoise-clad group nearest me, where a man in a violet mantle of cheap satin was dancing alone, and suddenly his gestures were significant and his face was noble. After all, why not? All dedication is the same, and the nostrils of heaven snuff impartially burnt offerings and incense, sweat and gardenia. I saw the American soldier watching, the dancers parrot bright beneath his khaki shoulders. He was tall and golden as a god, a fair-haired Quetzal among his Indios, intent and solemn as they. It was as though this were something he understood, this striving and this dedication, as though the man in the violet mantle, and the Indio there kneeling his way along, and he himself were all pilgrims. By now, inside the church, the Lady was enthroned again in a misty glitter of prayer and diamonds. She was a high symbol, a flag, and outside in her honor danced the Indios in their garish, gaudy uniforms, and the American boy watching in his khaki dress stared at them, and his eyes were huge as the ocean, solemn and lucid as the eyes of Quetzal the god from across the sea.

A dancer fainted; they threw water at him, and he got up and went on dancing. I had forgotten all about Verna, but now I suddenly saw her. She was staring at them, at the man who had fainted and the man with the thorns in his palms and the American boy, and her face was no longer a fashionable face, it was intent as theirs. She looked at me.

"This is something," she said. "I guess I hadn't realized—"

And then, suddenly, she was gone. I followed her through the crowds to the church doors and into the church. The floor was thick with kneeling pilgrims, and up by the altar, amid the swinging tides of incense, moved priests in copes glittering like seashells. I saw Verna threading her way between the Indios, stepping over them. She reached the great bank of flowers that hemmed the altar steps. The Indios were staring; the acolytes gaped at the foreign woman, with only a scarf tied crookedly across her hair; and one or two junior priests gathered in a little knot, as bouncers do. Verna passed between the banked flowers and up the steps. Nobody stopped her. At the altar's foot, below the high place of the Lady, between the snowy flowers and the serried white shafts of the candles, whose flames shone all together as one flame in a vague haze of gold, she stopped. Her head was bowed, but she did not kneel. I saw her hands fumbling. And then there was a glittering in her fingers, and a ray of green flashed from her square emerald as she laid it on the altar.

Part II: AUTUMN

15.

NOW, in the fall, we were in a sort of second spring. Trees came into bud, the papayas were fruiting, the violets were in second bloom, and on the shore there were small clumsy calves and frisky foals and baby burros with puzzled faces. One of the foals, with a white blaze between its eyes and a brown coat the texture of a very expensive velvet carpet, stared at me for a startled moment and then hurried round behind Mama, whereupon Mama, without bothering to find out what had scared her offspring, gave a hearty hind kick, just in case. The duck was sitting, and Silvanito unearthed a clutch of turtle's eggs from somewhere. Yet this was not an unusual fall. We had some real autumnal days, brisk, blue skied, fresh. But the clouds were still hanging about, and the sunset plunged its rays into still, shineless water, where colors were drowned, leaving on the surface glimmers and glitters proper to seashells, soap bubbles, and opals. On one of these evenings I got out my little collection of opals and turned them this way and that, catching echoes of the opalescence of the lake.

Not many people like opals. I always suspect that many who will not confess to the superstition nevertheless, in fact, entertain some unconscious fear of them. To me they are among the most beautiful of precious stones, alive with "the bright fire of the ruby, the splendid purple of the amethyst, the green sea of the emerald, all scintillating together in an incredible play of light," as Pliny described them. The stone is curious, for though it is usually tinted with some pervading color, its glitters result, not from any pigmentation, but simply from the refraction of light in the cracks that fissure it. The more cracks, the more glitter. It is delicate—both soft and brittle—and it is also porous, so that it must never be immersed in any liquid.

Until the discovery of the Australian fields, all Europe's opals came from Hungary. Nowadays Australian stones are the most prized, but I own some beautiful Hungarian opals in which the most brilliant fires flash through a milky mist. Since I like opals, I have naturally found my way in Mexico to Querétaro, where I have invariably spent my time poking about in all the shops where opals are sold so that, till recently, I had never visited the Hill of the Bells with its chapel erected on the spot where Maximilian, Miramón, and Mejía were executed. Mexican opals are not good. Few can really be classed as gem stones, and many have only a few gleams of fire. There are quantities of yellow-red ones, which I call salad opals, for their tomato tones are usually shot with lettuce green. There are many, too, whose filmy red and brown shades suggest tea barely tinged with milk. There are some, pale and watery as moonstones, which have no glitter, but which, at certain angles, flush with a uniform glow of color like the opals of Hosako in Japan, and some of these are very charming. There are also blue, peacock-flashing stones, but these are usually small. However, if you find in opals the fascination that I do, you can pass agreeable hours in Querétaro, turning over the stones and occasionally bargaining over some scrap of blue flame, some glass-pale cabochon that, as you turn it, sheens all rose and lilac. Your pleasure will not cost you much, and whenever you turn out your store you are in the magic cave of all the fairy tales. The trouble is that, though I always mean not to, I somehow often give my Mexican opals away, and then I have to go to Querétaro again. On this occasion, looking at my stones, I saw that I still had one that showed the change rather than the play of color. I remembered that Doña Chabela had said she had never seen one, and I decided to give it to her.

Doña Chabela is sentimental, hot tempered, generous, mean, cheerful, and romantically devoted to tombstones all at once. She is immensely energetic and is always doing twenty things at the same time. She has a week-end house in Ajijic. The Cornishmen who many years ago worked the silver mine built at the foot of the hills a house, which after their departure fell slowly into ruin. This was bought by Doña Chabela and her husband. They repaired it in spots and added to it in spots, so that it is now a rambling structure full of surprises. Every now and then Don Sergio thought he would add a coal shed, or Doña Chabela wanted what she called a laboratory for extracting her honey from the combs, or they thought they would have a new dining room. But the room never fulfills its destiny, for every weekend they come down from Guadalajara accompanied by hordes of friends and relatives, and sooner or later every room becomes a bedroom. Doña Chabela herself is very knowledgeable about cooking and about everything to do with a garden, a huerta, bees, poultry, cattle, and crops. I have often asked her help or advice, and she constantly sends me presents of fruit from her well-tended trees.

The next morning I walked slowly up the village and on to her house. I found her in the patio.

"I know what you've come about," she said. "That pit the workmen left when they were getting gravel to fill your terrace. It would be troublesome to cut a drain all the way down to the shore, and spraying the water that collects is ugly and expensive. In just a minute I'll tell you what to do." As she spoke she fastened three buttons of her housecoat, one of which at once came undone again, releasing a bubble of pink flesh. "I'll come back at once. I left my typewriter down in the garden last night. Look, here is a copy of the *Raza de Bronce*. I don't believe any poetry can be as beautiful as Spanish."

She swept off, followed by five or six children who had been standing about in the patio, and I started to read Amado Nervo's rolling lines about the Indio, the *Race of Bronze*. A man and woman came in from the road, said good morning, sat down, and began to eat grapes, throwing the pips on the tiled floor. A fat woman pulled a bed out of a room and began to make it in the patio. From the kitchen, where about a dozen people seemed to be cooking at once, came the sounds of terrific frying. Suddenly Doña Chabela came back, carrying a hen.

"Look," she said, "the poor thing. She's new and all the others have been pecking her."

The hen had a deep wound on the back of its head and seemed very frightened. Doña Chabela went to the cabinet radio, opened it, and found a Worcestershire Sauce bottle.

"Luisito," she called to a small boy I hadn't noticed and who was half asleep in a rocking chair, "go into my room and bring me the cotton. It's on top of a sack full of corn, with Sergio's old hat, or else it's in that big sugar crate with my knitting and the garden hose. Now—"

She poured alcohol from the sauce bottle over the hen's wound, using an enormous quantity and splashing it all over the floor. The boy brought the cotton.

"Now fetch some banana fiber," she said.

The boy went out into the huerta. After a few minutes a girl, considerably older, came with the fiber, and Doña Chabela tied a rakish bonnet of cotton over the hen's head. Then she produced a bit of string from a drawer, tied one end to the hen's leg and the other to her own ankle.

"I brought you this opal," I said. "You see, it looks like water, but turn it and it's all almond green."

"Can I pick some oranges?" asked the girl. "Oh, did I tell you my mother is coming today, with my three brothers?"

"Everything's full," said Doña Chabela. "I don't know what we can do. What a lovely stone. You need banana trees," she added to me.

The boy called Luisito came back with the typewriter, which was covered with mango peelings. Doña Chabela flicked off the peelings, put a piece of paper in the machine and began to type furiously.

The man and woman who had been eating grapes finished them and got up.

"Now we're going," they said. "Until presently, Chabe. Where can we buy a little pig?"

"Tiburcia has one," answered Doña Chabela, still typing. "She lives down by the church. Do you like the book? Mexican poetry is very beautiful. Bananas soak up water. I shall treasure this opal."

From a drawer of the table she produced a little box of cough lozenges and put the opal in with them. Suddenly a woman in black satin arrived. She had an elaborate hair-do, and had obviously come straight from the city.

"Chabe!" she cried, throwing wide her arms.

Doña Chabela jumped up, and for a few minutes all was embraces and laughter and little cries of "how good to see you again" and "what a miracle." While the hen tethered to Doña Chabela's ankle flopped and fluttered.

"I was just writing to you," said Doña Chabela. "Now I needn't. I present Señor Chandos. Conchita, a relative of mine."

"I've come for a week," said Conchita. "Have you a little bed for me? Or shall I sleep in a tree with the fowls?"

"Of course, Conchita," said Doña Chabela. "You shall sleep with me, and Lolita and Lupita can go with Tere and Bibiana, instead of Dora, and she can go with the cook; she's very tiny, and the cook has fleas but no bugs. Oh—I'd quite forgotten Carmencita said her mother and three brothers were coming today—well, we'll put a wide bed in the new henhouse for them. The plaster isn't quite dry, but never mind. Now sit down and tell me everything you've been doing."

They chattered away, and members of the party drifted in and out of the patio, some of them greeting Conchita with streams of emotion, some of them just saying good morning and not being introduced. Carmencita arrived and asked for some playing cards, which Doña Chabe found in the cupboard of her night table. The fat woman came out into the patio, said "Well, it's you, Conchita," and pushed her made bed back into her room. A man who had not appeared before, in brown trousers, pink shirt, and purple suspenders, came out of a bedroom holding a bottle of beer. He looked balefully at everybody, spat, finished the beer, and threw the bottle into a tub containing a withered palm with two wet bathing dresses and a paper bag hanging on it. Then the priest arrived to call. He wanted some honey for his cough. He sat down with us. Suddenly Doña Chabela started typing again; Conchita and the priest chatted. This went on for some time. Then the priest jumped up and turned pale.

"It's just a little wounded hen, padre," said Doña Chabe, still typing. "Did she peck you?"

The man who had drunk the beer fetched another bottle from a carton on which a bantam cock had been perching, opened it, and swilled noisily. The man and woman who had eaten grapes came back, leading a little pig on a string.

"Look, Chabe, we bought him," they said.

At last I got up to go.

"Won't you stay for lunch?" said Doña Chabela. She took the paper out of the machine and tore off the lower half. "I have written down all the instructions for planting banana trees in your pit. They'll suck up all the moisture. And here's where you can get good ones. It's a friend of mine, a most cultured woman, who has a house in a big huerta on the outskirts of Guadalajara. She lives there all alone with three dogs and sells plants of every class. She has very beautiful hydrangeas. Don't forget to take the book. Poetry transports me to the stars. By the way, while you were away Don Amílcar left his shop. He asked me to tell you. He's not going to be a butcher any more. He's gone to Los Altos where he has an uncle. You know, up there all the houses are built of hewn stone, and the people have eyes as blue as morning glories. My friend is a most honest woman and you can deal with her with every confidence in every way, but don't pay more than one peso less than she asks for each banana tree. They should be a meter high—if she has any, that is. I don't think she has just now. But you could get some hydrangeas, though they aren't any good in your pit. You must promise to come to lunch another day. We have lunch at two, or three, unless it's late."

Certainly Doña Chabela changes and glitters like the most lively opal. I always enjoy seeing her.

16.

ON MY way home from Doña Chabela I met Avelino. He is tall, thin, melancholy looking, and, stiff and starched though he looks, he dances the jarabe tapatío beautifully with Tiburcia, the wisewoman. I don't think I have ever seen him smile. He owns various little patches of land, he makes bricks, and he is always immaculately dressed in the old Indio way, with clean white pajamas, ironed into the proper small squares, a dull blue sash and huaraches. Some time before he had come to ask me if I didn't want to buy a plot of his land, which lay outside Ajijic toward Chapala. I had been to see it. It had a good lake frontage and commanded the whole wide view, and the morning I was there a score of white herons, as graceful as fans and as unpleasant to one another as human beings, were fishing along its edge. It had a few trees around the sides but was otherwise quite bare. Eventually I had decided to buy it. Of course, there were the usual complications. In the first place, a strip of the land belonged to somebody else, from whom I had to buy it by separate treaty. Then it was found that Avelino had raised a mortgage on it, and the holder of the mortgage had to be dealt with. And after all that it turned out that the deeds were not in the name of Avelino at all but of his daughter. I had just received from my lawyer the papers she had to sign.

"How not," said Avelino when I explained to him. "I take the little papers and bring them all in order the day you indicate."

We agreed on a day for me to take him to Guadalajara so that the whole transaction might be completed.

"When you pay me the centavos," he said, "I am going to put new bamboos under my roof of tiles, and buy another cow, and make a little excursion of eight days to the capital, because I have never seen it."

I went on to my house. After Doña Chabela's bear garden, the patio was a pool of peace. The accustomed sounds—Candelaria's distant monotone, the Professor's typewriter, the rhythmic cracking from a corner where Tippet was having an illicit bone—were the merest murmurs. At the door of my room Nieves was waiting for me, looking rather apprehensive.

"Come, señor," she said, and led the way onto the terrace.

There is a niche in the back wall of my terrace, fitted with shelves, which we use as a parking place for all the oddments that accumulate—pruning shears, packets of cigarettes of uncertain ownership, odd pencils, magazines, and so on. All these things were stacked on a table, and the shelves were full of plaques of Our Lady of Guadalupe, brightly painted and gilded. I found that they all had price tags on the back.

"That señora from Chapala, the one they say is a duchess or a countess, did it," said Nieves brightly. "Can you give me some lamb's wool?"

"What ever for?"

"My mother has a hemorrhage of the nose, and nothing will stop it, not cold bandages or alcohol bandages or anything, and they say she should breathe the smoke of burning lamb's wool. I've seen some inside those little shoes of soft leather, pues, that you wear in your bedroom."

Rather grudgingly I snipped a small part of the lining out of one of my bedroom slippers and gave it to Nieves. Then I gathered all the plaques into a basket, and in the evening I took them down to Rendel's in Chapala. As usual a party was going on. Rendel himself was painting, but on the terrace one big group of people was playing noisy gin rummy, several more were listening to the radio, Edwina Schwert was sitting on the edge of the lily pond, dabbling her toes in the water and singing in German, and everybody was drinking. I couldn't see Lady Connemara.

"Denise? She's gone out to get something in the plaza," boomed Rendel from behind his easel and was detached by a wave from Martha Inchbold, who already had a gaggle of young men in tow.

I waited, looking out over the brilliant garden. The water lilies close at midday, and the pond was studded with piled green pads, but on each side the cannas shone pink and scarlet and yellow and orange. Daylight was going, and they shone with deeper and deeper tones. I found Rendel again.

"Denise? She's in the bath," he boomed and was beckoned over once more by Martha.

Nadeen Braze, with her pile of red hair beginning to slip its moorings, tried to rope me into a little talk about Chirico, which she was giving to nobody in particular. After a minute or two of this I interrupted her to ask, once more without much success, about Lady Connemara.

"Denise? Oh, she went to Guadalajara this morning and won't be back till tomorrow. Be a lamb and fetch me another Cuba."

I had given up all hope of getting anything done and was preparing to leave messages when I heard a voice from upstairs.

"Hey!" it called. "Come up here."

I found Lady Connemara on the roof terrace, apparently making mud pies. She had a wooden trough full of mud, and she was mud to the elbow.

"This is a special clay I got out at Tonalá," she said. "It's very easy to work and fires well, and I am making a number of small images of Our Lady of Guadalupe. I paint them after they are baked, and I think they ought to sell very well, don't you?"

She had several more finished—flat-backed plaques of the Virgin in her great oval Gloria. I said I thought the tourists might like them.

"Oh, yes, of course," she answered. "They can give them to friends at home or wear them as costume jewelry. But I mean to make the Indians buy them. I shall price them low. Three pesos." I could not help thinking of the two-hundred-dollar dress of which she was making such a mess. "Now tell me," she went on. "Don't you think I could bake them in that old German's oven?"

I said I would ask Mr. Humpel.

"I went round myself," said Lady Connemara, "but he wasn't there, so I just popped a few plaques into the oven and left them."

I thought Mr. Humpel might not care about this, so leaving my basket beside the trough with muttered regrets that I could not find room for a showcase on my veranda, I hurried off home to straighten things out. I was too late. As I came in from the garage, Silvanito came into the patio at the half run he uses instead of a walk, carrying a note and a can.

I opened the envelope and read:

> In my oven not today used, I found the six (6) figure cakes of worked loam now sent in herring tin. Please counsel all that the oven is my particular and return tin. In spite, be advise that I stay the next month (November) also.

I returned the six clay figures to Lady Connemara with a polite note to say she couldn't use the oven for her baking. The following day she came up to see me, and I showed her Mr. Humpel's letter.

"Surely it was the most natural thing in the world," she said. "The old Hun wasn't there when I went, so I just popped my figures into the back of the oven, where they couldn't be in the way. Of course, I intended to warn him that they'd need several bakings. And by the way, Mr. Chandos, you owe me twelve pesos. Four of those plaques you brought back to me the other day were broken when I came to take them out of the basket."

I saw no reason why I should foot this bill, and though I'll do much for a quiet life I refused to pay her. She went off to interview Mr. Humpel, and in the evening he came to see me about her.

"The Lady Countess Connemara wishes to bake her apparitions in my oven," he said, groaning louder than usual. "It does not convene me, for I like my alone life, but I wish always to live at peace with the neighbor for my soul's sake. So I yessed her desire but said she must replace the fuel extra used. Pennies I do not wish, but the coals and kindlewood."

I said I thought that was a very reasonable stipulation.

"For when she sends to bake on my cook days," he went on, "I have asked three kilos of coals and half a kilo of wood, conditioned that there are not more than twenty little mud pictures and that you as house possessor have nothing there against. Last night, with my colded beer, I took a strong thing and today I am ever running. So please give me excusion."

I heard no more for several days, and then one morning Lady Connemara burst, unannounced, into my room where I was sitting at my desk typing.

"Look at this," she said, thrusting a crumpled sheet of paper into my hand.

I read:

> Honored Madam Countess! For neighborness sake I was conform that you should bake your figurettes in my bread-oven, but to find earth everywhere I did not await. There have gone to the dogs two of my loafs entire, and four (4) roserolls, all mudded, for which you are to me indebted $2.60 of national money, which please to send, for today I was climaxed to find your virgins reposing on my pumpernickel.

"Did you ever hear the like?" said Lady Connemara. "I leave you to deal with the bill—"

I thought that was enough.

"Yes, all right," I said, "I'll settle up with Mr. Humpel. But on one condition: namely, that you leave this house now and don't come back—ever."

17.

THERE was a knock at the door.

I can often guess my callers by their knocks. Aurora, when she comes with the washing, taps timidly as if expecting to be scolded, and somehow she manages to transmit a sigh from her knuckle onto the door panel. And I always know the madwoman, who comes every day to collect her tortilla sandwich from the kitchen: she has a conversation with the door, and chuckles at it before she knocks. Venustiano strikes the door firmly, says, "It is I, may I pass?" and then sits down outside and waits. But this knock was none of these. It was a knock like thunder.

"It's a little one, señor," said Nieves, coming into the room carrying her dust pan and a newspaper, "and he says if you don't want to buy this periodical?"

I hadn't seen a paper in two weeks, and it was only a day old.

"He asks ten centavos," said Nieves.

But when the boy had gone, I found he had left me only the second half of the paper, the sports and murder section. Later I found he had sold the front half to Venustiano—also for ten centavos.

The next morning the boy brought a paper again, and I

went out to see him. Again he offered me the back half of a day-old newspaper.

"You only left me half the paper yesterday," I said, "the half I didn't want, and you charged me ten centavos, the price of the whole paper."

He was a bright-looking boy of nine or ten, I judged. He was wearing a very clean white shirt of a strong cotton material they call Indian's head, and the rest of him was filthy.

"But now it is easy, señor," he said. "Now that I know the pages you want I can arrange with another to buy the other pages—many prefer them. It is very simple. I go and come."

He was back in a flash, carrying the front half of the Guadalajara newspaper and eating a radish as big as a turnip.

"Yes, that's the part I want. How much?"

"Ten centavos," he said and spat out a piece of radish.

"But that is the price of the whole paper."

"How not, pues."

"Well, this is only half of it."

"That yes, yes, señor," he said, taking another bite at the radish. "How else do I make my little negotiation?"

I paid him the ten centavos. Newspapers had never come regularly to Ajijic, and I welcomed the chance of getting one daily. I agreed in future to pay him twenty centavos for the whole paper, and every day for two weeks a paper came. Sometimes it came in the middle of lunch, and sometimes it arrived after dark. Usually the boy delivered it himself, but sometimes his younger sister brought it. And once his mother brought it.

"Today," she said proudly, "my children have both gone to school. Wouldn't you like to buy this little woven basket as well? It's very fine."

For nearly a month I received my day-old copy of the newspaper regularly, and then one day it didn't come. Nor in the morning of the day after that. But in the afternoon the boy marched into the patio.

"Bulmario Sánchez to serve you again, señor," he said, grinning with pride and holding up a bunch of that day's newspapers. "Look you, señor, now they catch the early bus from the city. Now already, today, for only twenty-five centavos, I bring you the little periodical of tomorrow."

18.

AN UNEXPECTED guest arrived. His name was Fordyce. He was thirtyish, tall and pale, and he looked as if he expected at any moment to be offered an insult, which he was ready to repay with a hefty kick. I thought that perhaps after that he might feel better, but I did not feel sufficiently self-sacrificing to try my theory out myself. He took the remotest room, disappeared into it, and sent to ask for supper in bed.

Thereafter he seldom appeared, and when he did, he hurriedly crossed the terrace and went for a walk on the beach, rarely acknowledging a greeting. If the terrace were empty, he might sit down there, but as soon as he saw somebody coming he got up and left. All the newspapers and magazines went to his room and stayed there till Nieves brought them out. He ate mostly in his room, but every now and then he would appear in the dining room and sit at a small table in the corner with that kick ready. If I asked him whether his food or the service had been satisfactory, he hesitated a moment, studied the far side of the lake, and said in faint bored tones, "It was all right, I think."

Mrs. Fountanney asked him if he didn't think the view magnificent.

"If you like views," he said.

The Professor told him his wife had been stung by a hornet while picking peaches.

"What else did she expect?" he asked.

We told him Lady Connemara would like to invite him to lunch at Rendel's.

"Old cow," he said, which I took to be a refusal.

Mr. Humpel said, "The young man does me sorrow, for he weighs too light. I like to send him this fine German butter-made cake."

Fordyce returned no thanks to Mr. Humpel, but he ate the cake.

Lady Connemara buttonholed him on the beach, when he was caught between a wall and the herd of goats, and asked him what he was doing here in Ajijic.

"Minding my own business," he said.

19.

WE WERE suddenly very conscious of the existence of the jail, for a day or two later Cayetano's buddy Primitivo was in it. It seemed that, returning home toward eleven at night, he met a friend of his, somewhat drunk and on the point of quarreling with several others in the same condition. Primitivo took his friend home and then went back to his own house and to bed. But the next morning he was sent for by the comisario. This was a new comisario, one Don Fidencio, who, as the owner of cattle and property, was a prominent citizen and was displaying considerable energy. He had imposed a curfew, insisting that villagers be in their houses by eleven, and, in the interests of public order, he had given each of the four divisions of the village a chief and a subchief. Primitivo was put in jail while his friend and the drunks were rounded up. But then, in Mexico, innocent bystanders are often kept in prison as witnesses, pending the investigation of a crime or accident. At midday Primitivo was fined two pesos and his friend five.

"Paz hasn't a centavo," said Cayetano. "And since she jumped out of the window"—Paz had eloped with Primitivo some years before—"it has given her family much anger and she can't go to them. She doesn't know what to do, and Primitivo's father hasn't any money in effective, so can I have two pesos from my bank, please?"

For two years now, in an effort to make Cayetano save money, I have kept, from time to time, such small sums as he manages not to spend out of his weekly pay. Two or three times this savings account has reached quite respectable proportions, but twenty pesos seems to be about the limit. Once this is reached, there are always a number of sudden small expenses that reduce the balance to mere centavos again. It is rather like the old game of snakes and ladders. One or two good tips from guests, a skillful deal with his fishermen friends over a question of some kilos of whitefish, or even a week's careful living, these are the ladders up which his bank balance mounts. Then the snakes sting it—a new pair of shoes must be bought or a brightly colored shirt for party occasions, a fiesta is held at San Antonio or a friend is married, and Cayetano is once again at the foot of the financial ladder.

I gave him two pesos. "But how unfair," I said. "Why should Primitivo be fined?"

"It gave him much anger," said Cayetano, "and me too. But what can we do? You see, with most comisarios the fines are for themselves, but Don Fidencio is rich and he wants to paint the school, so the money goes for that. If he has people in the jail, he has the labor too."

Cayetano was worried about the fine, but he evidently saw

nothing extraordinary in the comisario's methods of collecting fines and workmen.

"But has the comisario a legal right to impose a curfew?" I asked. "Surely that is done only when martial law is proclaimed."

I could see the sense of the rule, however, even if it were illegal and I told Cayetano so. He shrugged his shoulders.

"Perhaps it is good," he said. "It keeps order. Of course it does not apply to us or the señores, your guests. It's for the villagers and country people from outside, who don't know how to behave and get drunk, causing disturbances. That way it is very good. But as for Primitivo, he has done nothing wrong at all."

The comisario's job is not an easy one. He has to tread a middle path. He has many duties to perform and must be firm, but the village will not tolerate officiousness.

I remember one comisario who considered himself unable to deal with certain difficult cases and hired the services of a tough for this purpose. Although the village didn't much care for it, all went well until the first fiesta. The tough got violently drunk and started a fight. He stabbed several people, and only the force of numbers prevented further casualties. He was overpowered and taken off to jail. The comisario became the laughing stock of the village and shortly afterward resigned.

His successor did not fare much better. He was turned out for being too energetic. This was little Don Pedro, whose reign coincided with the building of my home. He loved Ajijic, he was a good man, and his sense of justice was keen. One day an Indio boy, a foreigner from another state, came to the village to stay. He had money and he spent it, and he often got drunk. In his cups he was boastful and, no doubt, somewhat lacking in courtesy toward Ajijic and its people. Certainly, one evening, when he climbed our wall brandishing a gun and shouting that he had full powers from the President of the Republic to shoot whom he liked, his manners were more than dubious. Cayetano pulled him down by the heels, and he spent the night in jail, apologizing in the morning in the prettiest way imaginable and making the improbable statement that he had drunk seventeen bottles of tequila. I suppose he would have apologized just as prettily if he had killed somebody. He was not persona grata in the village, and one night he was found in the street with seven dagger wounds in his body. Don Pedro, who had heard all the noise from his house, told his family to open the door and see what was the matter. Now, if a villager hears cries in the night, he burrows under his sarape and looks to see that his door is bolted: he does not go out and investigate. There have been too many revolutions and bandits for that. Besides, to go out means that you have intervened, and even if you don't get into the fight, you will get into the inquiry about the fight. Don Pedro, however, urged his family to go out and see who was groaning in the street. But he himself was ill in bed, his family was afraid, and nobody opened the door.

So the boy bled to death. Two men, universally considered the culprits, confirmed suspicion by fleeing to the mountains.

Now in Ajijic there are no soldiers and no police. Authority is vested in the person of the comisario, usually elderly, and his young secretary. When somebody is intolerable, the village takes the law into its own hands. Nobody knew who started the fight on the night the boy was stabbed, and indeed Don Pedro himself declared later that, even if the boy had been the President's own brother, he had asked for what he got by his overbearing manner. Nevertheless, he sent to Chapala for soldiers.

They stayed in Ajijic for a week—two of them with an officer. In the daytime they searched the hills, returning at sundown to bathe and wash their clothes on the beach. They were very clean and self-reliant. I talked to them one evening. They both liked being in the army; one, I think, because he felt important, and the other because he saw so much of the country, having often been sent as a guard on trains. They had both recently been out for some weeks in the wilder parts of Jalisco, down toward Ciudad Guzman. The method was to send a detachment out from one town bound for a distant one. On the way it stopped in each village, and if there had been a crime they stayed until the affair was closed or the criminal caught. Thus their tours were of uncertain duration, and meanwhile they had to look after themselves, cooking, washing and mending on their own.

One evening the soldiers didn't return from the hills until late, and soon the news went round that they had sighted the murderers and shot them. Though there is capital punishment in Mexico it seldom operates, and murderers are often "shot while trying to escape." The village, however, resenting interference from Chapala, was much pained by the swiftness and savagery of the reprisal.

"Why," they said, "it wasn't a bad murder at all."

And Don Pedro, too, was forced to resign.

20.

AVELINO had come to say that the papers for his land were now in order, and on the appointed day I picked him up to drive into Guadalajara to see my lawyer. He showed me his daughter's signature on the papers.

Avelino does not often go to the city, and he was a little flustered. First of all we went to the market, for, with the posada now full, I had a huge list from Candelaria, and another from Cayetano, who keeps such things as DDT and kerosene, and in addition I had to get everything from liquor to soap. It is not often possible to park the car very near the Corona market, and anyone buying for many days ahead has far more than he can carry. But this difficulty is catered for. A score of boys, of any age from ten to fifteen, roam the market, offering to serve as porters. They have no fixed tariff; you tip according to load and distance. They have a communal store of big round wicker baskets that they carry on their heads, and the loads they can take are astonishing. One boy of thirteen I know thinks nothing of carrying about twenty pounds of vegetables, two four-pound cans of cooking oil and three five-liter demijohns of tequila. But you must take a little care, for it is a point of honor to say that no load is too heavy, and a skinny little shaver may undertake to carry half a mile a burden he oughtn't to carry half a block.

As I was walking to the market, I met one of these boys, carrying on his head a full basket. He spotted me and suddenly ran across the street, leaving his current employer gaping.

"Are you going to the market, señor?"

"Yes."

"Will you use me?"

"Yes, if you're around when I get there."

"Will you go, as usual, straight to that Sebastiana, she of the vegetables?"

"Probably."

This business over, he rejoined his startled employer, who had no doubt fancied that he was making off with her goods. I continued slowly toward the market, and when I arrived the boy was there. He was carrying a basket and following another marketing woman. He took no notice of me at all.

I made my purchases and hired another boy to carry them to the Hotel Morales, where I am allowed to keep them for the day in the icebox. Then I found I had lost Avelino.

I returned to the car, but he wasn't there. Then I went back to the hotel, for I had explained to him that it was there we were going to meet the lawyer in the afternoon, but Avelino wasn't there either. Nor were my purchases.

"Oh, yes, señor," they said, when I telephoned the market, "they must have arrived by now. The boy left an hour ago. It was that Paquito. He is of confidence, señor, and his mother has a crooked leg, but she is always here on Fridays to sell her little painted turtles of the coast."

I waited about the hotel for an hour, and then I shopped for a few things that were conveniently near at hand. There was still no sign of Avelino, nor of my parcels. I had a drink, and then lunched off an excellent cheese omelet. Now good grating cheese is difficult to find in Guadalajara, and even then it's expensive. I asked the waiter if he knew where that cheese was obtainable, and he called the housekeeper from the kitchen.

"Oh, yes," she said, "this is a very fine class of cheese. But who knows where it came from, señor. You see, it was delivered to the kitchen in a big parcel of groceries and bags of many other little curiosities that I hadn't ordered. Oh, yes, it is of the most fine."

And so it was. My lost groceries, instead of being left at the front office, had been delivered to the kitchen. I had eaten my own cheese.

After lunch I went up to the market again to look for Avelino. In the city nowadays it is rare to see a man dressed in his sort of ranchero clothes, and many people had seen him, in different places. I looked in all the cantinas and eating booths, and at last, a block from the market, I found him, eating a cucumber that had been cut so that it opened like a flower, and bandying pleasantries with a whore who was leaning out of an upper window. She was telling him that it was too early in the day, and he was saying that five pesos was very dear anyway, a city price for gringos.

I got him away, and we went on to the appointment with the lawyer, an old man with a beaked nose and a bald head crowned by a great brown mole. He looked at the papers Avelino had brought. The daughter had signed in the right places.

"She's not married?" he asked. "Because if she is, her husband might object to the transaction, and we had better have his signature too."

"Oh no, she's not married," said Avelino.

"Does she live with you?"

"No, not any more."

"Where does she live?"

"She doesn't live any more," said Avelino. "She died three months ago. She was in a truck that turned over and fell right down a barranca."

Tears came into his eyes, and he made the sign of the cross. The lawyer stared, scratching the mole on the crown of his head.

"But here's her signature, dated the day before yesterday."

"Yes, just as you said."

"But how can she have signed it if she died three months ago?"

"She didn't sign it," said Avelino, "I wrote the name myself, with great care, in the presence of my friend Don Prisciliano Pérez, who witnessed it."

21.

FOR some time it had been increasingly difficult to get gasoline, and, having none, I had to go to Guadalajara by bus. I asked Cayetano if there weren't one that left Ajijic about nine in the morning.

"No," said Candelaria, "at eight thirty."

"That's the Phantom," said Cayetano.

In Mexico you will often see trucks and local buses whose drivers have written pet names on them. The truck that collects my papayas for the market in Guadalajara is called El Mister, the one that brings my lime from Chapala is The Bird without a Song, and the mineral-water truck, simply, Delirium.

"But the Phantom is sometimes very late," said Nieves. "That is why they call it thus. Sometimes it doesn't pass until the next day, pues."

"It won't go tomorrow," said Cayetano. "Tomorrow is the fiesta in El Chante, to which you said I might go in the afternoon, so the Phantom will stay in El Chante, with all certainty."

"All the buses go there tomorrow," said Candelaria. "They say there won't be any in the other direction at all, that is, none except Don César's new bus. That goes to Guadalajara."

"Are you sure?"

"Oh, yes," said Cayetano, "it has to go to the city every day because it also carries much freight, and if it didn't go the freight would throw itself to lose."

To make quite certain, I went up very early the next morning to inquire at Don César's house. In the yard, a young man was sitting on a crate of tomatoes behind a desk, drinking milk out of a gourd.

"Oh, yes," he said, "it goes every day without fail."

"What time does it leave?"

"At ten, pues," he said, and then, as an afterthought, added, "but who knows, for it doesn't have limits."

"It wouldn't leave before ten?"

"It might. Last Wednesday it left very early, but that was because Don César was going to see the Governor about the new school."

I asked if he thought there were any chance of its leaving early today.

"Oh, no. Sometimes it doesn't leave until from eleven onward."

"But it will go to Guadalajara? It's not going to take people to the fiesta at El Chante, like all the other buses?"

"Oh, no, señor. Look, it's here now."

I went home to breakfast, and when I returned to the plaza at ten o'clock there were already a number of people in the bus. I got in and found myself a seat between an old man who was nursing a big straw bundle and Chui, from whom I used to buy my milk, who was taking some cream cheeses to Chapala. And then I waited.

A woman got in carrying a bucket of pig's entrails in one hand and a huge bunch of white lilies in the other. She sat down next to Chui, who cut one of the cheeses he was going to sell in Chapala and offered her a slice.

It was a quarter of eleven.

"D'you know," I heard Chui say, "at the finish and the end, I think I'll go on to Guadalajara too. My cheeses might sell better there."

"How much d'you think I'll get for these?" said the woman indicating the entrails.

"Who knows," said Chui.

"Pues," said the woman, "I'm going to the city to buy a new shawl, but my centavos won't reach unless I sell the flowers and these little tripes."

At a quarter after eleven the driver of the bus appeared, jumped in, and started the engine. Then he stopped it.

"Just to see if it wanted to go well," he explained.

Then César himself arrived. He looked inside the engine. He poured in some oil out of an old flower vase and started to talk very fast with the chauffeur. They talked for some time.

The driver started the engine again and turned to address the passengers.

"Says Don César," he announced, "that at the finish and the end, he has a mind to go to El Chante."

There was a slight pause, and then a flurry of conversation smothered his next sentence. Chui was guessing aloud how much he would get in El Chante for the remaining three of his five cream cheeses, and the woman next to him, firmly clutching her bucket of entrails, was arranging with a small child to take the lilies up to the church. Among the score of passengers for Guadalajara, there were only two who got off the bus with me.

"I can't go," said one of them sadly. "I have to go at once to the city. Last night a fit struck my mother."

22.

MR. HUMPEL went his way, sending little cakes to people who praised his parrots. He had come to terms with Lady Connemara, and she had made me a present of one of her larger images, with a label marked five pesos on the back, hoping, I think, that I'd forget having ordered her out of the house.

"It is the size I let the Indians have for three," she said, "though I made Doña Arcelia pay three fifty. She's got plenty salted away. I thought you could hang it on your terrace for your guests to see. What an extraordinary old man that German is. He didn't want rent for his oven; he wanted me to replace the charcoal and kindling I use. And now I find that the heavy rains this year have made them especially dear just now, so he'll have to wait a while. Ah, here's Don Bernabé. I've been wanting to meet him." She regarded him with her head on one side, cautiously; then, fishing an image out of her bag, she pounced. Her salesmanship is of the aggressive sort, but it had little success against the airy courtesy and expansive evasiveness of Don Bernabé.

"With the present augmentationing of prices, Señora Condesa, it is not prudent to allow oneself articles of luxuriousness," he said. "But the little statues are pretty. They are precious, exquisite, divine."

"In orders to buys, I permits to pay fifty centavos by week," said Lady Connemara, standing no nonsense from Spanish verbs.

Don Bernabé smiled, bowed, admired and bought nothing, and Lady Connemara went away crossly in search of more willing victims. Don Bernabé accompanied me into the huerta, where his son Merced was putting the finishing touches to the henhouse, the repairs to which had been delayed on account of the works undertaken, all in vain, on the house of the unfortunate Lupe.

Don Bernabé skipped up the steps, smiled, pointed his toe at the drying cement floor and skipped down again. Something in his posturing suggested to me the antics of the dancing masters of a hundred years ago.

"You will see, señor," he said, as the blood-red sarape swirled about him, "that the little house is of the most robust, with full impenetrabilitationing against the rains."

It was just as well that I had this work done, for, though the rainy season should have been ending by now, almost every evening we had storms with brilliant displays of lightning, and one night we saw a flash shaped like a tall, narrow croquet hoop with a fuzz of what looked like brush lightning at the top. This excited the Professor, and he went around talking to all the guests about it, quite forgetting the hissing insect he'd been stalking all that afternoon.

We had a number of visitors who stayed a few days each—two Mexican families in the usual Mexican pandemonium; a Lithuanian who had set up a doll factory, but who was having a holiday because he had made two thousand doll bodies and couldn't get any heads; and an Austrian monarchist who spent all his time writing poetry, in which our black-and-sulphur orioles and our black-and-orange butterflies appeared merely to evoke the black and gold of the Hapsburg banner; and a quartet of New Yorkers who stayed a week and sat indoors the whole time playing bridge. On the whole my guests were pleasant people, who, in the Professor's words, "traveled with a view to finding the things they did like rather than the things they didn't." The posada was very profitable, but it needed a lot of attention. I found that, though I was not occupied for anything like the whole day, it was impossible to settle down to any writing, for every fifteen or twenty minutes there was some order to be given, some work to be revised, or some decision to be made.

In October, it's true, I had contrived to finish *Village in the*

Sun. But other work made very slow progress. In its own way running the posada was a full-time job, and, though I was enjoying the new experience, I regretted the days when I couldn't find time to write anything, and I felt the liveliest sympathy for little Manuelito, the son of Tesifonte, whom I found one morning sitting on the beach in front of his father's field of chick peas, weeping and every now and then throwing a stone at the mud hens to drive them off.

"Otherwise they come in and eat everything," explained Tesifonte. "That is why Manuelito is not at school. He was progressing well, they said, and he likes the teacher, and every afternoon he was practicing, writing several words together, like a sentence. It's a pity. But I can't be here much at this time, and if he goes to study, we shan't have any chick peas, and then what?"

23.

THE GAS situation got worse. There were noticeably fewer cars on the streets of Guadalajara, the taxis would only take you for short trips at treble price, and outside the filling stations there were queues half a mile long. César's truck was reduced to two journeys to the city a week.

"It's the black market," screamed the newspaper. "They have a corner in gasoline. It's a disgrace to the country."

And the next day the same paper said it was all due to the Pánuco River, which had overflowed its banks and destroyed the road, thus preventing gasoline coming by truck from

Tampico. Even if it hadn't completely destroyed the road, they added, the river was so swollen that it was too dangerous for the ferry to cross.

"They say that the Señor Governor is taking it all for himself," whispered an old Indio to me. "They say it's for the machines on his little melon gardens, down on the coast. But who knows, pues."

"Many units of the North American fleet are exercising off Manzanillo," my lawyer in Guadalajara told me. "The entire oil supply of Mexico is being diverted there to feed them."

"It's the lack of tank cars," screamed the newspaper. "So many have gone to the States and not come back that there aren't enough to bring the oil up from Tampico. Our rolling stock is a disgrace to the country."

"The station in Guadalajara," said a rival paper, "is full of tank cars full of gasoline, but there's no one to unload them. It's a disgrace to the state of Jalisco."

"The pipe line from Tampico to the capital has broken itself," said Don César. "I'm sending my truck all the way to the coast to buy three thousand liters."

And then a Mexican tanker was reported on fire and, later, sunk in the Gulf.

"Of course," said everyone, "it was bound for New Orleans. Of course, it had a cargo of oil, otherwise why would it burn?"

But the next day they changed their minds.

"It was," they said, "the ship that brings oil from Tampico to Manzanillo via the Canal, and now it has sunk and there is no other ship."

"They say that many things now go to Russia," said Venustiano. "Or China, would it be? One never knows, one year with another."

I myself spent a whole day of fruitless search for gasoline in Guadalajara. I had been told that all you had to do was to obtain a priority ticket. "Say it's for the little motor to irrigate your huerta," I was prompted. I got a priority ticket easily enough, without giving anybody a tip, but I soon found that everybody else with a car had one too. There was still no gas, and I arrived back in Chapala with just enough in my tank to take me on to Ajijic. I went straight to the Widow's cantina and, over a long cool drink of lime juice, told her my troubles.

"Gasoline?" she said, and let out a tremendous catcall.

A policeman, who was sitting under an umbrella on the beach, got up and ambled over to us.

"Gas?" he said, "but you can get all you want right here in Chapala. Oh, no, I know there's none at the filling station. You must go to the cinema. I'll go with you and show you."

We drove the four blocks and I pulled up in front of the theater.

"Not here," said the policeman. "We must go to the back door. Oh, no, we can drive round. It's the black market, you see, so we had to stop them selling it out here in front. Sound your horn."

A man came out bearing two enormous cans, and, without my saying a word, filled my tank. He charged me about fifty per cent above the normal price.

"Thus it is," he said. "It isn't really dear. Whenever you need anything like this come to me."

"Oh, yes," said the policeman, slapping him on the back, "this Don Policarpio has many little hidden stores."

"Very well," I said. "And tell me, why is sugar scarce now?"

"Oh, that's because the growers can get more selling their cane to the makers of cheap tequila than to the sugar refiners. In the United States they are drinking much tequila that isn't true tequila at all."

"And so we have no sugar?"

"That's it," said Don Policarpio. "But if you want some now I can let you have fifty kilos. Would you prefer it granulated or in little lumps?"

24.

"THEN I shall buy twenty little centavos' more of bread," said Candelaria when I told her I was expecting extra visitors for lunch.

"Yes, Candelaria, and another liter of milk. How much is it a liter now?"

"Fifty centavos, except on Sundays when it's sixty."

"Twenty for bread, and the milk, that makes seventy centavos, doesn't it?"

"You will know, señor."

An hour later she returned and handed me thirty centavos change from the peso bill I had given her.

"I spent seventy little centavos, señor. Is that right?"

"Yes. You bought the bread and a liter of milk?"

"No. Two liters of milk."

"Then you've given me too much change."

"No, because I didn't bring the bread."

"It's still too much, because two liters of milk would be a peso. You shouldn't have any change at all."

"The other liter was for Valentina, the mother of that Nieves. But, of course, I paid for that with her centavos."

"Then, if you didn't get the bread, how can one liter of milk have cost seventy centavos?"

"It didn't. It only cost fifty, which is what I told you it cost. Then there was the bread."

"But you just said you didn't get the bread."

"No, but I've paid for it already. And I got these three eggs. Look you, señor, how they are of big. Oh, no, I paid for them with the centavos of yesterday, that is, for two of them, the other is a present from Doña Dimna."

"Who ever is Doña Dimna?"

"She of that Guadalupe Paz. They want to ask you a favor. Do I tell them to pass? They're outside now."

This time they came for a loan of thirty pesos, but I said I would only lend them ten. I said that was quite enough, that they didn't want to get themselves too deeply into debt.

"Money you don't borrow, you know, doesn't have to be repaid."

"That's right," they said, and, having thought about it for a minute, roared with laughter.

"How ready the señor puts himself," said Doña Dimna.

We went through the ceremony of signing the book, and then there started between them an argument. It was not acrimonious, but they shouted at each other a good deal and Doña Dimna repeated what I had said several times to her husband as if she had just made it up herself.

"But with thirty pesos," he said, "I could buy the shotgun."

"I said I'd only lend you ten. What d'you want a gun for?"

"To shoot a skunk with, pues."

"For Tiquico, señor," put in Doña Dimna. "He has fever."

"But what has Tiquico's fever got to do with shooting a skunk?"

"To cut the fever," she said. "He has a drying up of the nerves and very much fever, and for that the lungs of a skunk, boiled, are a remedy of the most best."

I said I was sorry to hear about Tiquico, and that I would try and go round to see him later, and added I was sure they needn't buy a gun.

"No," said Guadalupe Paz, "I don't believe we need," and added quickly, "But we shall need the ten pesos for sowing later, puesen."

"What are you going to sow this winter? You promised to tell me."

"Some little chilis of humidity, señor," he answered. "Those that one plants so near the ebbing lake that they suck its water and create themselves out of pure moisture."

"And," said Doña Dimna, "in that season you are still so

busy sorting and storing your maize that you scarcely have time to cook your beans, and even your tortillas you buy from another."

"And what happens if others are busy sowing their corn too?"

"Then the children make them, but children never throw in enough lime and the tortillas come out sour sour and you don't eat nearly so many."

"Well," I said, "that's an economy."

This, too, was an enormous joke. They shrieked with laughter.

"Ay, what a señor!" sighed Doña Dimna. "Válgame Dios."

"Then there's the coffee harvest," said Guadalupe Paz. "That is in January, the season when we untire ourselves. We pick coffee for a week and rest for a week, pick for another, pues, and untire ourselves again, and if there are any beans left over after that, then those are the ones that make the best coffee. And we always have a mind to cut a few adobes at Christmas, but we don't make them till January, because the earth has more force when the year has turned."

"Don't you like the little roots of the hill, señor?" interrupted Doña Dimna. "Puesen, winter is the month you should send to the cerro to dig them."

I said I liked them very much and remarked that I thought my coffee would be ready for picking this year in December.

"Oh, no," they both said together.

They seemed quite shocked.

"Oh, no," repeated Doña Dimna. "Forgive me, señor, that I put myself disrespectful, but it is not so."

"Why not?"

"Some coffee bushes may ripen in December, but not yours, pues."

Both fell silent.

"But how d'you know?"

Neither answered.

"Pos," said Doña Dimna at last, "with all certainty your coffee beans won't blush till January, señor."

"They say, puesen," said Guadalupe Paz, and he was really agitated, "they say that only the beans of a stolen coffee tree ripen in December, pues."

25.

MONK, the puppy, suddenly decided that she liked the taste of petates, the straw mats I use to cover the tiled floors, and she chewed holes in half a dozen of them in a single morning. I arranged to make a trip to Sayula in the car with a few guests, to buy some more.

Our way took us along the coast road, where, at the end of the rainy season, you wind and bump through every luxurious mood of lakeside scenery, at one moment moving through the lacy shade of acacias between lush fields of head-high green corn and orchards of papayas in slender, well-drilled ranks, and the next moment pinned in the narrow stony track between the steep myrtle-green hillside and the pewter sheen of the lake itself. Then we ran along a strip of the Mexico-Guadalajara highway until we came to another rough road leading up over the pass to Sayula.

Even in its views Mexico is unexpected. Here, there was nothing of the gradualness with which the first Italian panorama opens up after crossing an Alpine pass. We climbed five hundred feet over a stony road, turned a sharp corner, and the view burst upon us, entire and breathtaking, in an instant. Forty miles away, across the huge basin that lay scooped out below us, the snow-capped Pico de Colima towered above the gray-lilac mountains that basked around the valley. The lake of Sayula looked, for all its size, strangely humble. From so far above, its shallowness seemed pitiful—a smear of thin gruel in the middle of a colossal dish—and all around it lay the acres of smooth rose-gray sand that once formed its bed. For Sayula is a dying lake, shrinking from year to year, drying up. Now, at this season, the lake bed was over half full, and the fields that lay around it stretched vivid green right to the mountain wall. The well-ordered villages with their criss-cross lanes looked tinier than anything the Lithuanian's toy factory could ever produce.

We drove down the pass, and at the second village along the lakeshore we found a small manufactury of petates. These mats were woven in a herring-bone pattern from the stout reeds that formerly grew very plentifully here. They were mostly made to a size of about five feet by four, and many Indios have never known any other bed. I asked the price.

"You will know, señor," said the man, a Tarascan whose eyes were so dark you couldn't see the pupils.

"One peso," I said.

"Pos, that's very little, señor. The little reeds are very scarce just now. One fifty."

There followed a little polite bargaining, and at one thirty we agreed. I bought a dozen and packed them in the back of the car.

In the evening, as we drove back across the pass, I wondered how many more years the reeds would grow at Sayula and the greenness of the valley floor would continue to refresh the eyes of the traveler and give work to the inhabitants; for when the lake finally dies the valley with all its life and its wealth will die also. Disafforestation, bad cultivation, injudicious drainage works have created havoc throughout the Americas. The old Maya civilization perished, it is said, through soil exhaustion. Soil erosion has done its best to ruin much of the Mississippi basin; the drainage of Lake Texcoco, too, has helped to spoil the climate and amenities of Mexico City. Here at Sayula it is easy to prophesy the creation, for the self-same reasons, of a man-made desert out of one of the fairest valleys of Mexico.

It was after eleven when we reached Ajijic, and I was tired and unprepared for any fresh experience by the time I got to my room. On the bed, in the midst of the counterpane, was what appeared to be a large lump. All sorts of thoughts ran through my mind: Tippet, a practical joke, a rattlesnake, and that last, quite unnecessary glass of tequila in Jocotepec. I pulled back the cover. With one leg cocked vertically over her shoulder, Minou was engaged in extensive washing operations. She rose purring with the smug, self-satisfied air of an amateur conjuror who has successfully performed a particularly clever trick, and made as though to butt my hand with her ear. There was chaos in the bed, and four squealing kittens.

I suppose I should have noticed before that something was afoot. Normally Minou is of a notably odd shape, very thin—though God knows she eats enough—with long kangaroolike legs that arch up her body in a gangling manner. It is not the sort of figure in which violent fluctuations of line should remain unnoticed for long. Besides, all the previous week she had been taking an inordinate interest in every cupboard in the house, and once she'd come flying out of Fordyce's room pursued by a rich variety of tart and unprintable comment. But I had fondly imagined she was looking for mice.

In Ajijic the Christmas celebrations extend, in all, over several weeks. The posadas start on December sixteenth and last until Christmas. According to tradition, groups of singers go round from house to house, singing and begging in the name of the Holy Family for shelter—posada. When they are admitted, they are given food and drink, and then there is a party. This is now seldom done, and a posada is customarily a party like any other, with music, refreshments, and dancing. The only time in Mexico I ever saw or heard the traditional procedure, with songs and processions, lighted candles and all the rest, was in the American embassy under Ambassador Daniels, and then most of the participants were Americans. The Ambassador had organized everything in the best Mexican tradition, except that there can certainly never have been a Mexican party without drinks, and Mr. Daniels as always served no liquor. The prudent had fortified themselves before coming.

Here the old custom is merely an excuse for nightly celebrations, and it is preceded by the feast of San Andrés, Ajijic's patron saint, and the three days' observance of the day of Our Lady of Guadalupe, which falls on December twelfth. Christmas passed quietly and pleasantly, and even Mr. Humpel raised an uncertain voice in "*Stille Nacht, Heilige Nacht,*" and the Professor wore a paper cap out of some snappers.

Around the New Year business at the inn slackened off. The Fountanneys were going away for January, and as I had no immediate bookings, I decided to use some of the money I had made and go down to Oaxaca, leaving Fordyce and Mr. Humpel on their own. They were perfectly satisfied with this arrangement; in fact, Fordyce said he'd be delighted to have a little peace and quiet.

Then Silvanito wanted to go away too, to the children's fiesta at Cajititlán. This takes place on January sixth, the Day of the Feast of the Kings, because the church there contains life-sized images of Melchior, Balthazar, and Caspar. They are all joined together and are carried round the village on a plank. Melchior is black, Balthazar red, and Caspar white. Silvanito explained to me that on arrival you go to the nearest house and reserve sleeping space by throwing your petate on the floor. The villagers make no charge for this, regarding free accommodation as an extra inducement to bring people to the fiesta. But of course if you get there late you have to sleep out of doors.

"There are many big tents of saloons of dance," said Silvanito, "one enormous of big, with a domed roof like a church. It's a very pretty fiesta, especially for such an ugly little village, for ugly ugly it is, with a very small lake that has nothing in it but catfish and a few canoas that leak. But the people there put themselves very ready. They spend very little on the fiesta and buy only very small firecrackers that make hardly any noise at all. All the same it is very nice, and there are many wheels of fortune and roundabouts and Hungarians, and you spend a mountain of money. How many centavos of wages would you owe me, señor?"

I told him and his round face lighted up.

"I shall be able to divert myself very well," he said. "That is, if you permit me to go. And would you pay me in advance for the week that enters?"

Now everywhere in Mexico the Day of the Kings is the children's day, and traditionally a Spanish child, instead of putting out his stocking on Christmas Eve, should put out his shoes on the Eve of the Day of the Kings. I asked Silvanito if many children went to the fiesta.

"Oh, no, very few, because people go there to divert themselves, and children are a great nuisance because they try to put themselves into the diversion too. Most people of the village even shut up their children during those days so that they shan't go to the dances or get their thoughts scrambled by the Hungarians."

"And how many days do you want to be away?"

"Oh, the fiesta is only for one day although the music starts the day before. Last year I only stayed a short time, just three days, because I had to leave, because it had taken me other days to dig the roots of the hill for the centavos with which to hire the burro to go, and when I got to the fiesta, I sold all my eggs at once, and the next day I had only tomatoes to sell. Most people stay the whole week, buying or selling, and the music goes on as long as there are people to dance. But since you will want me to guard the house while you are away, I could with all certainty be back on the fifth day, or the fourth. And don't you want to lend me your old impermeable, for the January rains might come, and you often lend it to that Cayetano."

"And I was going to ask you, señor," interrupted Lola, who had been eavesdropping, "if you wouldn't lend it to me instead."

"What," I said. "Do you want to go too?"

"Oh, no, señor. It's only that this Silvanito is a careless boy as all the world knows, and has already, of this month, lost a fork and broken a fine olla, watering his little seeds. The fiesta too is much very bad. You know, two years ago, or maybe three, I took my sister's children, the poor little ones [they are undoubtedly Lola's own]. There were many people so that we could get no lodging, and there was much noise. And the tequila too was of a bad class, for I drank several little glasses myself."

She belched reminiscently.

"I took the little ones to a roundabout, and there we saw three peons from El Capulín, very far taken in drink, who were speaking to all the women with such disrespect as children ought not to hear. And indeed among those people of up there in Cajititlán it was a most foolish thing to do. They spoke to me too, but I went away at once and pulled little Jesús and María up into a tree to sleep." She paused to swat a fly with her duster and added with a little sigh, "And the peons were too drunk to climb up after me—or much else."

"How long did they keep you treed, Lola?" I asked.

"Pues, I slept all night, though they told me next day that there had been many bothers and disgusts—even shooting. I woke up early in the morning, before the sun, but still they danced and the music played down in the plaza. Imagine to yourself though, señor, how strange it was to me to see those three peons dancing up there in the tree beside me. At first I thought it was the tequila I'd taken, but I soon saw it was only the morning breeze, for there they were, all three of them, hanged by their necks from the branches round about me with their tongues sticking out and their faces as purple as plums."

Interlude: PLUME DANCE

26.

I HAD heard that the road to Oaxaca was in bad repair, and since anyway I don't like motoring long distances alone, I drove down to Tehuacán, a flat, uninteresting place, noted for its mineral waters, where I left the car and took the narrow-gauge railroad that goes to Oaxaca and no further. It is a run of about eight hours through varied but not very interesting country. We arrived punctually, with the result that there was no one at all at the station, which lies a little way outside the city. The passengers descended, the engine whistled, and then down the road came a cloud of dust, rolling ever nearer, from which detached themselves the station official, the porters, the hotel touts, and the small boys hoping for odd jobs, all running like mad, followed by a few weary cars. How could anyone have guessed the train would be punctual?

Oaxaca lies at the junction of three great valleys, which were once three lakes, and above it hangs the height of Monte Albán. Here the Zapoteca and Mixteca had their fortress, overlooking the trade routes between the Valley of Mexico and Yucatán, and here they seem to have lived, exactly like the Nabataeans of Petra, without toiling or spinning, but simply by exacting tolls from those who passed. These lakes were not drained by the Spaniards. They were drained by a Zapoteca king called Zaachila, and a considerable engineering feat it must have been. He did not create a sandy waste but a fertile valley bottom and moved his capital down from Mitla, and after the Conquest the Church knew a good thing when it saw it.

The glory of the city of Oaxaca is its building stone. This is a pale almond green and lends itself readily to elaborate carving. Most of the principal buildings are made of it, fresh and cool as leaves after rain, and, with the many pink-washed houses, make of the city a rose garden. It is also one of the few Mexican cities whose cafés have tables on the sidewalk. Why there are not more of these throughout the country is incomprehensible. There is hardly a Spanish village without such, and the Mexican climate is more appropriate than the Spanish to them. Many cities have arcaded squares, which lend themselves to this agreeable arrangement. In Oaxaca, however, you can sit in the plaza and watch the variegated crowds go by. And very variegated they are. Here the Indios are different from the Indios of Jalisco. Their skins are lighter amber and honey and old gold, and they have fine small bones, so that often they have a Cambodian air. Here, on market days, you can see costumes from all about, from as far even as Tehuantepec, two or three days over the mountains. There are sarapes of many sorts and colors woven here, but I think the handsomest are the ones that are off white with discreet and graceful designs in black. Almost all the women wear their shawls twisted into turbans on the head. And the sashes of Oaxaca are gorgeous. In the market they flutter in gaudy rows high above the stalls, in all the reds you can imagine—scarlet and crimson and burgundy and magenta—and in all the pinks, lilacs and purples too. They run the course of heather, from budding pink to fading mauve, and take in all the sumptuous royal shades as well.

It was January, but the weather was perfect, and of an evening I could sit out on the plaza until midnight without an overcoat, listening to the band playing in its little gimcrack stand and watching the passers-by—wild-looking Indios from the hills and prosperous citizens with their wives and daughters in black satin dresses and with black satin eyes that shone with a brilliance undimmed by too much reading. Indeed, at all times of the day, I very easily found my way back to the plaza, for it is the center of life, and everything and everyone passes through it sometime or another. I went up to Monte Albán in the daytime to see the excavated temples, and in the evening to see the sunset from the Plumaje, a high spur that was the lookout whence the old robbers watched for caravans. I went to the museum to see the Treasure, jewels of gold and jewels of jade, exquisitely wrought, that were found in a tomb on Monte Albán. I went to the Church of Santo Domingo to see the fantastic ceiling carved in high relief, which depicts the tree of the Dominican order, its roots issuing at one side from Saint Dominick's stomach and its topmost branches at the other side resting on the Virgin's heart, while other branches terminate in effigies of kings and benefactors of the order, and all round stand wooden statues of Dominican saints and popes. I went out to Mitla and wandered in the oblong rooms whose walls are decorated with lacy geometrical carvings, graceful and restrained and of never failing invention. I saw the Great Tree of Tule, of which they will tell you that it may be two thousand years old or it may be four, a Mexican cypress of enormous height and girth, and, close by, its hijito, or little son, itself a monster among trees. I went down to the bridge early on market day to see the burro caravans come in, scores and scores of them, with whole families along and sometimes a crazy high-wheeled cart. I went to see the linen weaving and the potteries. But I always got back to the plaza and sat there watching the show go by.

I had heard there was going to be a plume dance in the neighborhood, and that was something I was really anxious to see. Nobody seemed quite to know where the dance would take place, and twice I went out in a hired car to outlying villages to find that it had been put off, for lack of money, or lack of dancers, or just because it had been put off.

Once in Tlacolula I stopped to ask a venerable white-haired old man whether he thought the dance would take place or not. He was said to be the descendant of the Zapoteca kings, and I was told that he was perpetually municipal president since he was the person whom the Indios would obey anyway, so there was no point in putting anybody else in authority. He was a man of property, and owned a big house with an enormous yard. I found him, wearing white pajamas and seated on the high curb outside his house, watching a train of laden burros go into his yard. Before answering he watched the last of the burros go in and called out an order in the tone of those accustomed to command. Then he turned to me.

"I have given permission for it," he said and gave me a curt nod.

I bowed and went.

We drove slowly down the village street. Coming toward us I saw a young woman with an oval face the color of old ivory walking with grace in a faded flame-pink dress. She had some onions to carry, and she had tied them all together about halfway up the long leaves, and, as it was hot and sunny, she was wearing them as a hat, the bulbs circling her head like a diadem of giant pearls under the waving green plume of the leaves. The effect was not comic. It was smart and distinguished.

"Look at her, with her onions," said the chauffeur, a citified youth in a pale pink suit who didn't like going far outside Oaxaca. "It makes us Mexicans ashamed before you foreigners when the Indio bumpkins behave like that. And d'you know who she is? She's the granddaughter of that old man you talked to. Kings, indeed!"

Perhaps you have to be the daughter of kings to make a bunch of onions into a princely coronet, I thought, but I didn't bother to suggest the idea to the chauffeur.

On my return from this trip I found a letter from Mr. Humpel.

> Sir! On the 8st arrived two desirous guests (American). Of my own answering I gave them room east No. 1 and received their payment for two (2) days, being total with

extras 96.70 (ninety-six pesos seventy centavos Nacional money), which waits you, hoping I had right. On the 11st came Doña Chabela with many companions to make a dinner picnic on the terrace, where remained afterwards many rests. She bathed both dogs who are yet well and send a master-bark. She had the idea to bathe the badger, but he did not wish. Please be advise that for the end of the current month (January) I go. Hurry not to house, for all is in order. I thank you.

I wrote to Mr. Humpel, thanking him but saying that I had never intended that he should be bothered doing business for me, and went out and bought him a sarape. I meant to get a sensible dull-colored one, for Mr. Humpel's belongings were all plain and drab, but somehow I didn't. I got one of the off-white ones.

A few days later it was said that the plume dance was to take place at Cuilapam, a ruined monastery out in the middle of the big plain, and I set off once more. The dirt road led out through flat, dusty villages, mere collections of cactus-fenced yards with straw-roofed huts in them; but the monastery itself had trees round it, remnants of the cultivation of the monks.

The walls of Cuilapam are the yellow of a dried lemon. In the open space in front of the great pointed arch of the entrance, an entrance that now led only to a roofless hall, the dancers were standing about. At one side was a band, mostly brass, close beside a long trestle table covered with bottles and glasses. On the bank that surrounded the open space sat perhaps a hundred silent Indios, waiting. There were about forty dancers, divided into two groups, Indios and Spaniards, for the plume dance tells the story of the Conquest. The Indios wear trousers banded with ribbons, and tunics with short ribbon-banded sleeves, in reds, yellows, and purples, and belts set with brilliants. To shoulder, elbow, or knee are pinned gay silk handkerchiefs. And above all this glitter and flutter rises the headdress, a plain round cap worn over a knotted kerchief, mounted in front with a huge half circle of feathers, eighteen or more inches high. The bands of color follow the curve—scarlet, magenta, canary, white, hardly ever any blue or green—and among the feathers, round the cap, are set scraps of mirror glass. The Spaniards wear navy-blue, gold-braided uniforms with cocked hats, exactly like gendarmes of the Second Empire, but they too pin handkerchiefs on their epaulets or on their big trailing sabers and have mirror glass set in their hats and collars. There are two further members of the cast, two little girls. One is Moctezuma's faithful daughter, and she is in a bright satin robe clasped on one shoulder and wears a fillet with a panache of feathers in it. The other is the Malinche, Doña Marina, who became Cortes' mistress and betrayed her people. She is dressed to go with the Second Empire gendarmes, in a tiny crinoline of lilac satin, with a little lilac-satin bowler hat. Nothing was happening, and there was no sign that anything was going to happen. I waited for a long time, and still nothing happened. Then I went and had a talk with Moctezuma, who was also the local comisario.

Yes, he said, there was going to be a dance, or he hoped so. As we could see, they were all ready for it. But he didn't know what could be done, for, though they had raised all the money they could, there still wasn't enough to pay the band, let alone provide the refreshments needed by the dancers.

I was the only foreigner, indeed I was the only outsider present, and I was being held up. But I wasn't going to miss the plume dance this time, and after a little dickering, during which Moctezuma remained lugubrious, if not surly, fifty pesos changed hands. A brief animation seized the performers, and then they all drifted apart, and nothing continued to happen.

I sat on the running board of the car, where there was a little shade. The chauffeur climbed inside and went to sleep. It was late afternoon, the hottest time of the day. I could hear ice tinkling in the big jugs of poison-pink and lime-green drinks at the bar, but I didn't dare risk having one. I thought sadly of everything and everywhere that was cool and shady. Several dancers disappeared into the ruins. The little girl who was going to be Malinche burst into tears and was led away. Some of the dancers came back, and then some more went away. The chauffeur was snoring gently. A man arrived driving a burro laden with a big demijohn, and the bar became more animated. I hoped my fifty pesos had begun to work. Moctezuma took off his headdress. I waited.

Suddenly the band, or part of it, struck up the "Fiesta de las Flores." A trumpeter, who had been sitting with friends on the bank, jumped up and rejoined his fellows, playing lustily off key. Then they all stopped. But they had started something. In a few minutes the trumpeter tootled all alone, playing "Atotonilco." Then, apparently from nowhere, a large group of Indios arrived and joined the silent audience. A cornet and a clarinet joined in with the trumpeter. And suddenly all the dancers were there, the Indio group forming a loose oblong, several deep, and one or two of them began shuffling their feet. Moctezuma put on his headdress, the largest and most be-mirrored of them all, and gestured to the band, which stopped. But as soon as he had taken up his leading position, the music started up and so did the dance.

The step performed was very simple, two steps with one foot, two with the other, about turn, and the same again. It was trivial, but the splendid colors of the headdresses wove a glorious pattern against the yellow walls. From time to time a dancer who was tired or bored dropped out and went to have a drink or a chat with friends. After a time the music left off, and the dance went on to the beat of rattles carried by the dancers, and Moctezuma swung out of the dance and began to recite rhymed couplets in a high, singing monotone. The beating rhythms of the dancers and the dactylic tempo of the rhyme integrated the whole scene. The figure went on for about twenty minutes, and the effect was almost hypnotic. Then Moctezuma finished reciting, there was a sort of grand chain to inappropriate music, the cymbals and the drum crashed to-gether, and all the dancers wandered off at random, mopping sweaty faces and taking off their headdresses. There was a long pause.

Then the Spaniards took the floor, and I saw one I had not noticed before. He was about ten, and his uniform bagged around him. From one shoulder waved a Mickey Mouse handkerchief. This was the only modern note, except the mirror glass, and I feel sure the pre-Conquest Indios would have used mirror glass if they had had it. I dare say they would have liked Mickey Mouse too. In any case the Spaniards are so anachronistic in get-up, that it didn't matter. They are intruders. Nobody knows what the plume dance represented before the Conquest, what high ceremony of the solstice, what homage to what god. The church changed all that and gradually made the dance into the history of the downfall of the Indios. And you can see that the Spaniards are newcomers. Their steps are much the same, but the figures built of those steps are clumsier and have not the ancient sureness of the Indios' figures. They too had a spokesman who chanted, but there was no magic made by his chanting. When they had finished, the little boy came over to me, smiled shyly, fumbled in a deep pocket, fished out a battered cigarette, and offered it to me. He was the only person at Cuilapam who recognized my presence.

This time, for some reason, there was no pause. The Spaniards left the stage, and the Indios came briskly back and took their places. A young man with a Cambodian face just the color of Cuilapam's walls had pinned to one shoulder a turquoise-blue handkerchief. It was a startling note in this greenless, blueless color show. The procedure was much the same as before, save that not Moctezuma but another recited, in the same high voice. Then suddenly, as it does here, daylight went down. The white went out of the light, everything was bathed in pink-gold syrup, and the shadows turned purple. The change was sudden and as subtle as anything in the theater, and for the next half hour or so the lighting effects changed constantly, dimming one color in the banded headdresses, intensifying another, making a yellow shriek, dulling a red to chocolate, until the crossing rhythms of dance and chanting came out of the gray-lavender shadows, where scraps of white shone milk pale on moving ghosts. Then somebody brought a torch. More torches, a hurricane lamp, some kerosene flares appeared, and leaping, grotesque shadows pursued and mimicked the dancers; giant arms reached up the old ivory walls, baleful gleams sprang from the mirror glass, and it seemed as if steps and words went more swiftly, in a more urgent tempo. When the long figure ceased, it was like waking from a dream.

"Now it's dark," said the chauffeur, waking up. "And it's not only that the road's so bad, but it's dangerous to be out at night among all these savages."

I refused to leave and offered to stand him a drink at the bar. He said he wouldn't use the piggish village tequila to wash his feet with.

"Well, go to sleep again," I said. "We're staying some time yet."

The Spaniards danced again, and the little Malinche with them, making tentative steps and never taking her eyes off the nearest man—perhaps a father or a brother—and following his lead. Then there was an Indio figure, and between the prancing rows the other little girl, Moctezuma's faithful daughter, held tiny protective hands over Moctezuma's headdress, which he had laid on the ground and given into her charge, a symbol of his threatened kingship. The chanting became more plangent, a high wail from the dying Indios to heaven.

"Los Indios van pereciendo,
Diga, Señor, hasta cuando . . ."

And then came the battle.

Accompanied by the loudest noise the band could make, the two groups faced each other in triple line, the Spaniards with their sabers drawn, the Indios carrying wooden swords. Then they advanced upon each other, interlacing with the formality of a quadrille, clashing weapons at each meeting. They turned and marched again. It went on and on and became increasingly more like a fight and less like a court dance. The young man with the turquoise handkerchief chanted against the music, the wild lights flickered in an evening wind, and, as the weapons crashed, eerie shadows aped and exaggerated the gestures. A blade, a mirror, an eyeball flashed as a torch flared, and the crazy music of a popular song, the stamping steps, the high chanting, and the banging weapons blended into a nightmarish cacophony. It was fantastic and a little frightening. I forgot all about the theme of the dance, and the Spaniards, and the church under whose walls the dance was taking place. This was something older and deeper. I felt it was not being performed as a show for the silent, impassive audience; it was a ritual for a congregation. In some incomprehensible way it was meant. It was as though there had never been a conquest.

At last it ended, and the strange timeless magic went. It was already long after ten, and I had been told the dancers would dance all night or as long as the tequila lasted, with the performance getting more and more ragged. I decided that now was the time to go, on a climax. The chauffeur was relieved but out of temper.

"What are you going to pay me extra when we get back? If we do get back, that is, without meeting bandits or running into a ditch."

Nobody took any notice of our going, as they had taken no notice of our presence. Not a head turned among performers or watchers. As we backed to turn they were starting a new figure which looked like a triumphal march of the Spaniards. The little boy with the Mickey Mouse handkerchief swallowed a huge yawn, clutched his trailing saber, and fell into step. Bats were wheeling in the glimmering light above the weirdly lit stage, and nearby sounded the bark of a coyote.

"There's a place in Mexico City where you can see the dance much better done, with clean costumes and proper lighting," said the chauffeur, "but I suppose you didn't know that."

In Mexico City I found another note from Mr. Humpel.

Sir! Unknowing if Señor Fordyce has allowness to radio-play the whole day and night, I have not protested him. The batteries are now out. Else, all goes well, only that the good Candelaria has three days witch's shot and could not move the back, but the little Nieves made the kitchen with all calm. Both dogs are healthy and devour well. The Dackel I found nestmaking in oven, has she now her time? Please to instruct. My old parrot has a disgust with his woman, who before two days flew to a house in Royal Street where is a fine young man parrot. So are the women, and it is the Nature. Please be advise that for the next month (February) I stay also. Will you be so kind as to bring from the capital one-half (½) kilogram birdseed and three (3) pairs cheap cotton undertrousers number 42? I thank you.

HEINRICH JOACHIM HUMPEL.
Ingeniero.

Part III: WINTER

27.

AS THE car stopped, the hubbub started. The dogs came bounding in the fullest cry; the servants all came running out, Nieves with her mother, Aurora and her little daughter Trini, Obdulia, Silvanito in an old pair of Mr. Humpel's trousers, Lola, and Cayetano with his buddy Primitivo. The street was boiling with people, all talking and giving little cries of welcome. It was like being in a parrot house. Gradually the noise diminished, and then each of the servants had some mishap or some lack that needed to be reported instantly. I got out of the car with my arms full of parcels, and Candelaria started taking them away from me, talking all the time.

"How good, how nice, señor, that it went well with you. And how glad we are that you are back in your comfortable house. And I must tell you that I am leaving. It is indeed good that you enjoyed yourself in that place where you have been—"

"But, Candelaria, leaving? Why d'you want to leave?"

"I don't want to leave, señor," said Candelaria, taking the last parcel from me. "It is my mother, Remedios. She is sick, and I must go to her in Jiquilpan. I will try to wait until you find another cook, but it is my mother, and there was flesh of deer in the village today so I bought some against your coming, so did the Señor of the Oven, though what it will serve when he has cooked it I do not know—"

"I don't know what I shall do without you, Candelaria."

"It gives me much pain, señor," she said, starting to give the parcels back to me. "Remedios is sick or I would never think of leaving you. Indeed, she is very sick; she is most grave; she is at the door of death. But I hope not to leave you planted, and I am going to pound the little steaks of deer for they are very fresh."

Now I had been told by a former employer of Candelaria that, when she had saved up a sum of money, something urgent would recall her to Jiquilpan. I had also been told that it was useless to try and dissuade her, but that when the savings were gone she would come back.

"In Jiquilpan," she went on, handing me back the last parcel, "I shall sell charcoal and eggs and wood and cool drinks of many flavors. Remedios sends to tell you that with the new crutch you sent her she is able to walk much better—but of course just now she is agonizing. Ah, it gives me pain—"

And she scampered away to the kitchen.

It was a poor homecoming, for cooks as good and capable as Candelaria are not easy to find anywhere, and I had the Fountanneys returning and other guests expected. But there it was. The other servants, who looked as though an expected storm had failed to burst, forgot all about their lacks and mishaps and gathered up the baggage. When I had washed, I went to see Mr. Humpel. I found him with the badger sitting on his lap.

"Heartily welcome to your lake paradise," he said, and the little punctuant groans, about which I had forgotten, came at once as a surprise and as one of those familiar sounds, such as the whir of a mower or the bang of a gate that nobody ever mends, which are part and parcel of home. I realized that Mr. Humpel had grown into the place. He was delighted with the sarape.

"I am very content," he said. "I shall hang it on the wall. It is markworthy that, when I buy for myself, I buy always the practical, say-nothing thing. Yet I have beauty feeling. I warn you that in these days Señor Fordyce is very calamitous. He pecks at all."

I decided I did not want to be pecked at just then and went to sit on the terrace without seeking Fordyce out. But I was telling Cayetano about various plants I had brought for the garden when Fordyce came in from the beach.

"Hello," he said. "Back?"

I said I hoped he'd got on all right while I was away.

"Perfectly."

I said I was glad and asked him if he would have a drink.

"I never drink. Did you have a good time?" he said, and went away without waiting for a reply.

"The señor has very decontrolled nerves," said Cayetano. "In the village they think that somewhere he must have done something that did not suit him and is hiding."

"That's very unlikely, Cayetano. Contradict it when you hear it. And, by the way, I brought a little pepper tree."

"Oh, but, señor nothing grows under a pepper tree, for the little fruits poison the ground."

"I know nothing grows, Cayetano, nothing but coarse grass. But they're pretty and make a nice shade."

Cayetano looked doubtful.

"It's not only that, señor. But also that, if you work in the shade of a pepper tree, it gives you a headache. And it is yet more dangerous, for if while you are working in the shade of a pepper tree you should fall asleep, you wake up dead."

The next day was cloudless. In the afternoon there was a flash of lightning behind the mountains to the southwest, brighter than the sun. Minutes later I heard a sullen growl of thunder, succeeded by another louder, longer growl. A lace of white cloud mushroomed up behind Garcia and grayed as it spread across the sky. The sun went down in a mottled blaze of grape purple, black, and orange. By midnight it was raining.

"The cabañuelas, the January rains," said Nieves brightly the next morning. "My small brother already has much catarrh."

"They're late this year," I said.

"That is why they have put themselves so violent," said Nieves. "They say they'll last eight days, but they don't have limits. Sometimes they forget to come at all."

"What a sad day," said Lola lumbering through the patio swinging a bucket on a piece of cord. "Ugly! Ugly!"

It rained slowly all the morning. The willow trees, the ducks, and I seemed the only ones to enjoy the change, though the garden, parched by many long months of sunshine, gave off intoxicating scents, a hundred different smells mingled into one. Cayetano, who was perfectly well at breakfast, had a raging head cold by noon. The hens, sheltering under the dripping coffee bushes, pecked feebly at low ripening berries and refused to lay. Cormorants, in larger flights than usual, winged down the lake toward Jocotepec, while bevies of grebe swam beneath them, hardly ever diving, but swimming hard and purposefully as if making for a secret shoal of charal they had earmarked against this rainy day. An occasional scorpion, flooded from beneath his favorite stone, scuttled across the huerta to the safety of the dry wall. There were no fish in the shallows, and the blue-and-white herons, wading wing deep to catch them, were so hard put to find a meal that they forgot to be spiteful to each other. The red ants frantically pulled twigs and leaves over the entrances to their nests, blocking the interstices with the drowned bodies of their comrades. Indios, muffled in sarapes and straw capes, soaked up the rain like blotting paper, and looked as if they would tear as easily. A heavier gust of rain swept across the lake, and I saw two burros close in on either side of a little burro and stand there protecting him until the gust had passed.

"I've been stung by a scorpion," said Lola waddling placidly back into the patio. "Look how angry the flesh is."

Her whole arm was inflamed. I fetched some ammonia and told her to take three drops in warm water every half-hour.

"Ugly animals," she said. "Wouldn't you be going to cut your nails today?"

I handed Lola the ammonia.

"Thank you," she said. "Are you going to cut your nails?"

"Whatever do you mean?"

"You do from time in when. I've seen you."

"Why d'you want to know?"

"As a remedy," she said, "little fingernails are unbetterable."

I cut my nails and Lola boiled the clippings, mixed with roast tomatoes and chili, and made a hot poultice to put on her arm. By evening the inflammation had disappeared.

"Here is the ammonia," said Candelaria. "It smelt bad so we didn't use any."

The next day was fine.

28.

SEÑORA de los Bohorques arrived in a portly automobile, with a chauffeur, a maid, and a Pekingese, and announced herself as a relative of the González de la Comarcas. She was white haired, tall and upright, dressed in unrelieved black, and on her fingers, which were beautiful and much more youthful than her face, she wore several handsome diamonds in old-fashioned settings. She kept herself to herself and gave me no trouble at all, because when she wanted something she asked the servants directly. The maid slipped about like a shadow, and every morning the chauffeur washed the big car, whether it had been used or not. In the garage, beside my car, it had the air of a Great Dane being tolerant to a puppy. Every now and then the chauffeur washed my car too. The Pekingese was very aloof, and not even Tippet, who is the friend of all the world, could make him fraternize, and he and Monk ignored one another, even on the narrowest path of the huerta, each sniffing the air as they passed and looking into the distance.

Every morning Señora de los Bohorques had a big upholstered armchair taken out on the beach and set in the shade of the willows, and there she sat. She smoked a great many black Spanish cigarettes, but she neither read nor talked. Before luncheon she took a tiny glass of neat tequila, with some little titbit—slivers of cheese with olives or slices of avocado—which her maid prepared for her. She bowed to the other guests when she met them, went to Mass, and once a day asked for the radio to be tuned into the news. She listened without comment, bowed to anybody present, and withdrew to her room, where she spent many hours. After the commotion of some of my other guests she was a welcome change.

It was really by chance that I remembered her saint's day. I knew her name was Paciana, and I was reminded of the festival of San Paciano de las Flores when Cayetano asked for two days off to go to its celebration. I sent the old lady some flowers with felicitations on her "day of days," and in return she asked me to have a cocktail with her on the beach. When I arrived a second armchair had been brought out, the maid was hovering, and there were several kinds of canapé, including a horrid mass of minute, threadlike, whitish eels, which, when spread like a paste so that you no longer saw they were eels, tasted good. As a hostess, Señora de los Bohorques had manners of such gracious distinction that the tequila cocktail and eels took on the air of champagne and caviar, and I felt myself to be important.

The Spanish character is lyrical but not at all romantic. Like some splendid bird that, just as it seems to be of more than earthly beauty, dives to ground for a grub, so any Spaniard can speak in the phrases of a lyric poet, peppered with practical footnotes. Señora de los Bohorques talked like this, in a beautiful classic Spanish untouched by any slang, gesturing with her graceful fingers.

"I have known this lake, señor, since I was a girl, and when I have been unhappy, it has always given me comfort, as if its waters washed my heart," she said. "See, the sails of the boats as they come up over the horizon there—are they not like the breasts of doves? And now that the railways are in such a lamentable state and gasoline and tires are dear, the boats are doing a very good business carrying freight."

It is fairly safe with Mexicans of the age and sort of my hostess to talk about Porfirio Díaz, and after a while I led the conversation round to him. Señora de los Bohorques had plenty to say about the old days of the great haciendas and the month-long visits, twenty strong, the days when a man could go alone and unarmed from one end of the land to the other in perfect safety, for when traveling you just asked for a rural. He rode ahead of you, armed to the teeth, and, arriving in a village at nightfall, he roused someone and demanded a room. He looked after the traveler like a child. "Put your bed here in the middle of the room, there may be scorpions and animals in the walls, and I shall sleep beside you on the floor." He attended to food and everything. All this, with fodder for both horses, cost the traveler half a dollar daily. Then she got onto the centenary celebrations of 1910.

"At the great ball in the Palacio Nacional there were ten thousand invited guests. All the galleries round the patio were reception and refreshment rooms, and in the first-floor galleries we danced. The illuminations were the last word of their day. There were delegates from all over the world, and such jewels and gowns as now one can hardly believe ever existed. The men blazed with stars and ribbons, and the women were princesses from the country of the fairies. They waltzed in falls of lace and rainbows of gauze amid a rain of diamonds. And did you know that it was one of the first times that a card system was used for carriages?"

Just then Candelaria came bustling down to us.

"Imagine, señor—with your permission, señora—imagine what has happened. Don Odilón has left, and he has gone to his home, and what about the electric light, for who knows if that young brother of his can put on the motor?"

Now Odilón was the mechanic of the principal corn mill of the village. He was an excellent mechanic, and he did a number of odd jobs on the side. He had installed all my plumbing and electric wiring; he mended automobiles and radios; he dealt with sewing machines and typewriters. He had prospered and, besides owning various pieces of land that he rented out or worked with a sharecropper, he had built himself a house. You would have said he was sitting pretty. Mexicans will not infrequently abandon responsibilities or duties out of mere pique or caprice, but Odilón had seemed a steady sort.

"How long will he be away?" I asked.

"Oh, he won't come back, pues," said Candelaria.

"Why not?"

"It's like this," she went on. "His wife, that Socorro, has left him. It is true that he often beat her with sticks, but he had married her by law, puesen. It happened that the father of her first child has just returned to the village, and she left Odilón and went to him."

Candelaria paused, stripped a branch from a willow tree, and twirled it as a fly whisk.

"The father of her child had been away for three years. He'd been in prison, because he killed a man over there in Tizapán, or so they say, though they're very bad people over there anyway. But now he's out, and Socorro's gone back to him. So Odilón has left."

It seemed to me that Odilón was acting very foolishly. He was a good enough mechanic to get a job anywhere, but in Ajijic he had been very well placed.

"But what else could he do?" said Candelaria. "After that he couldn't stay."

"Certainly not," said Señora de los Bohorques, and the diamonds flashed on her fine white fingers. "No true man could stay. He had been shamed before the village."

29.

SUDDENLY Fordyce announced that he was going to Chapala and might not be back that night. The next morning Cayetano gave the little cough he uses to draw my attention when he has news to impart or a request to make.

"They say that the señor of here, the very rare señor, is in the lock-up."

"Oh?"

"They say that last night he was going round the streets of Chapala, drunken drunken, and at last the cops took him and threw him in the can."

The Professor had got the rumor by lunchtime. I said I had heard it.

"And what are you going to do about it?"

I said that I didn't know if it were true, that if it were and Fordyce wanted my help, it was quite easy for him to send to me, and that I didn't think he'd thank me for interfering unasked.

The Professor was pained. He was all for intervention.

"And what shall you do if he doesn't come back tonight?"

He didn't come back that night. But the next day we heard that Fordyce had spent the night in jail, but he had paid his fine in the morning, and he had had a long binge that day, lasting far into the night but avoiding the police. He had been seen in half the cantinas in town, drinking with most questionable Mexicans of both sexes.

"You must do something about this," said the Professor to me.

"But according to our information he's not in the prison, he's not sick, and he's not in any difficulty," I said.

The Professor worried at it like a dog at a bone, but for the life of me I couldn't see why I should go round nursemaiding my guests or trying to stop them making fools of themselves if they wanted to. I refused to do anything at all, and the Professor went so far as to say he was not sure that his conscience would not impel him to take action, but eventually it didn't.

"If you go to Chapala, Logan, you'll upset your stomach," said Mrs. Fountanney. "You know how those buses disagree with it."

Four days later Fordyce came back.

"Hello," said Mrs. Fountanney. "All right?"

"Perfectly," said Fordyce.

"We heard that you had been—er—arrested," said the Professor.

"Did you?" said Fordyce and slammed the door of his room.

In the days that followed he hardly emerged and then only to take a short walk. And a crop of tales came winging from Chapala. He had broken into someone's house; he had fallen off a roof; he had burned a boat on the beach; he had drunk three—or was it six?—bottles of hard liquor a day; he had bedded half the girls in Chapala.

"That's a very unhappy young man," said Mrs. Fountanney. "Badly brought up, of course, but very unhappy too."

Fordyce stayed in his room.

The gossip of the foreign colony went to town on the incident. Fordyce was a Russian agent, a British agent, an agent of the F.B.I.; he had deserted from the Marines; he had escaped from Siberia; he had bribed his way out of a cuckoo hatch in Mexico City. He was the life and soul of many a gathering he would never have dreamed of attending. He stayed in his room.

Venustiano said, "They say in the village that if that señor, the señor with the sad angry face, comports himself here as he did in Chapala, they say they'll beat him and throw him in the lake. Funny people, they often do worse themselves. But then they've always respected foreigners, until recently. To me, the señor seems a little mad, no more. Not much madder than most. The bad thing is, he doesn't pretend to be sane."

Fordyce's escapade was, however, soon forgotten in Ajijic. The very next evening there was a tremendous uproar. Shots were being fired in the plaza.

"Another fiesta," said the Professor. "D'you know I'm told they spend slightly more than half as much on fireworks as they do on milk."

In the morning the true facts came to light.

"Think, señor, just think!" cried Candelaria, setting down a basket of tomatoes on the breakfast table and putting on top of them a handful of small change, which rolled among the fruit. "Think! Last night they were killing a bull, a young bull, very strong, and he broke loose in Don Vicente's patio where they were killing him, and he killed one, poor thing, and to another he gave a big horning, and he broke the gate, and at the finish and the end the comisario shot him in the plaza! So what will we do since the Señor Professor has guests and Cayetano won't be able to wait at dinner?"

"D'you mean Cayetano got hurt?" I asked.

"Oh no," said Candelaria, retrieving five-centavo pieces from among the tomatoes and putting them on a pile of my manuscript. "But he has been up all night at the watch, and today in the afternoon is the burying, and he will have to go to that, and in any case he is too sad to do anything. He told me to tell you."

Candelaria looked at me as if I were unbearably obtuse and added a squashy tomato to the small change on my papers.

"But who was killed?" I asked.

"Why, Primitivo, of course," she said. "Cayetano's very great friend, his twin. And there is Paz, poor girl. What an affliction! Ay de mí!"

She went on for some time, telling me just where Primitivo had been gored, and how she proposed to arrange for the Professor's party, and how Paz had sat all night without crying, not a single tear.

A gloom settled over the house, and all the women servants gossiped in hushed voices, genuinely sorrowful, but also gloating a little over the tragedy of a girl who had seemed fortunate beyond their dreams. Paz, who never smiled but whose grave eyes held a kind of quiet laughter and whose cheeks seemed always ready to form dimples, had been the envied, but lovingly envied, of all. Widowed now at nineteen, she was still after three years of marriage the village's most beautiful girl, with a skin the shade of rosewood and a proud sweet face. Primitivo's parents were people of substance, and though, at first, her family had opposed the match, his romantic carrying off of Paz to his house, followed by a real church wedding, had ostensibly mended all. Primitivo himself was a good-looking, likable youth. He had once, when singing with a group of mariachis in Guadalajara, received the offer of a fabulous radio contract and had chosen instead to return home to Ajijic. Not very bright, perhaps even a little stupid, thought the village, but a good fellow, ready to help his friends, easygoing, honest. He had no need of any job I could offer him, but whenever I needed extra assistance, to fight the first lusty weed invasion of the rains or to wait at a party, he would come at once, and I had often seen him of an evening, unasked and unpaid, helping Cayetano, his boyhood friend, to wash and polish my car. Even after the birth of little Narciso, now a chubby two-year-old, he had remained, which is not common among the Indios, a devoted and faithful husband to Paz, and it had given one a little glow to meet them walking silently hand in hand along the beach, so young and radiant and content. It was a monstrous waste. Anyone in the village could have suggested several candidates for the bull's horns whom nobody would have much missed.

I went to Primitivo's funeral. It was not dignified. The Ajijic cemetery, outside the village toward Jocotepec, is a dreary deserted plot, a desert or a paddock, according to the season, with a few broken monuments that only enhance its desolation. The Professor and I trundled in the car behind the coffin. Cayetano was a pallbearer, but Paz didn't go.

"We wouldn't let her," said Cayetano, "for she might have an attack, a strong pain in the heart, and she might suffocate and be unable to walk, and then we should have to carry her on our shoulders, as well as the great weight of our sorrow."

The road is uneven and though, no doubt, the bearers did their best, Primitivo must have had a rough passage in his narrow box. And then the grave was too short. They tried to coax the coffin into it, but it was no good, and finally they had to excavate further. Personally I have no great respect for corpses. For myself and those I love, I would wish the bodies to be disposed of as quickly, cheaply, and unfussily as possible. To many, however, ceremony is a comfort, and I can see no reasonable objection to it. But a ceremony that, like this one, degenerates into the grotesque is, I feel, shocking. But nobody, except perhaps the Professor, felt as I did. The Indios stood around, solemn and patient throughout the service, and as the coffin was finally lowered into the earth tears ran down dusty brown cheeks.

30.

"What a barbarity!" cried Candelaria. "Imagine, five pesos fifty for one thin hen! I am very occupied making a book of recipes for the señor. I give you three fifty, no more."

There was another woman in the kitchen, and she had a fat black and white hen under her arm.

"Five twenty-five," she said.

Candelaria seized the hen from her, felt it all over, opened its beak, peered inside, and proclaimed, "It sees itself since at once that this bird is sick." She put the hen on the floor. "Look, she even stands crooked."

The woman picked up the hen, whose feet were tied together with banana fibers, and walked slowly out of the door. Candelaria watched her from the corner of her eye and, when the woman was halfway across the patio, said, "Three seventy-five is far too much for a little hen that is sick and thin."

The woman came back, and Candelaria grabbed the hen and began searching under its wings. Then she pinched it all over again and let it flutter to the ground.

"I give myself count that she flies crooked," she said. "And I didn't feel an egg inside her—oh, there's the señor—which means she's decomposed and can't put any eggs. Imagine to yourself, señor, this señora, who comes from across the lake from that village where they steal fishing nets, asks me four seventy-five for a thin hen that is sick and can't put. I offer her three ninety, no more."

"She's yours for four seventy-five," said the woman.

"That's what you said before."

"No," said the woman. "That's what you said. But I'll leave you her all in four sixty."

"Four pesos. I am very occupied because I am making a book with the señor. All the books of the señor contain many recipes which are mine."

"No," said the woman.

"Pues," said Candelaria.

And just when it seemed certain that terms satisfactory to both could never be reached, Candelaria dived behind a pile of garlics that were drying near the sink and counted out four pesos thirty centavos in small change to the woman, who counted the money again carefully and handed over the hen. Candelaria tied it to the table leg, threw it some dried crumbs of tortilla, washed her hands, and settled down to peel the potatoes.

"That's a good hen," she whispered to me. "Now I wonder why that señora sold her, for she'll cover at least fourteen eggs when she broodies herself, or sixteen."

Candelaria can build up a thriving poultry business in a few weeks. Though she had said no more to me about going home, she had been over to Ixtlahuacán the previous evening to say good-by to a cousin. Leaving that village very early in the morning with two sisal bags stuffed full of guavas and bottles of quince wine, she had broken her journey in Chapala, where she changed the fruit for sticks of cinnamon and some cracklings for which she had purchasers in Ajijic, and within a few hours of her return had set herself up in business with a capital of one black and white hen and small supplies of tequila, powdered horn, and turpentine in case the hen sickened and needed a dose.

"Just think, señor," said Candelaria a few days later. "Already my hen has a mind to broody herself. I'm going to throw her on some eggs."

The other servants say that Candelaria is lucky with her poultry. But it isn't only luck.

"I don't believe that the hen has the face of broodying herself," said Nieves.

"With all certainty she has," replied Candelaria, scornfully. "But, for the doubts, I shall tie her up near the fire so that she won't lose heat."

"How d'you tell when a hen is broody?" I asked.

"That's very simple," said Candelaria. "When she's been broody for two days."

And when the hen had been broody for two days, Candelaria went round the village buying eggs. She bought only long narrow ones because she said that those would be pullets. Then she tested them in water to see if they "sat well," and held them up against the sun to see if the yolks were the right color. She announced that the moment was ripe to set the hen.

"What luck," said Nieves, "that the hen is ready to throw herself on the eggs at the new moon."

"Is it luck," answered Candelaria, "that I know how to somuch a hen? No! Nor is it luck that the little hen knows at what season to broody herself. And you've forgotten the señor's coffee. Go you, run you!"

Of the fifteen eggs on which the hen was sitting, only one

failed to hatch out, and only one of the chicks was a bit wobbly on its legs at birth.

"What luck," said Cayetano.

"It is because I am a great worker," said Candelaria proudly. "I washed the eggs three times yesterday in warm water of herbs from the hills, and I threw a small sweet branch into the hen's bowl every day when she drank, and just before the eggs began to hatch she was very emotioned and I calmed her with a song."

Within a week Candelaria announced that eleven of her chicks were pullets. This time no one said it was luck. They just said it wasn't so.

The chicks grew, and Candelaria exchanged the three she said were cockerels for a young turkey whose mother had been eaten by a badger. Then she sold the one that had been "born little" and one of her bottles of quince wine, bought fourteen more eggs, and borrowed a broody hen, promising the owner to return her after two months, with the interest of three chicks, which he might select himself.

Her family of chicks grew, and every day she put fresh, dry sand from the beach in their coop and dusted it with a handful of my lime.

"And I shall sell the little droppings they make at night to Doña Dimna for her vines of passionflower."

Soon the chicks no longer needed their mother, who began to peck them. I suggested she be kept in my hen run.

"She'd be with the rooster and the other hens," I said, "and she'd start to lay again."

"But she's putting now," said Candelaria, horrified. "And then, down there, I couldn't watch her well. Oh, yes, she puts a little egg every other day without fail. One day with another I tie a string to her leg and throw her over Don Agapito's wall, with a very small handful of maize. His cock, that big colored one, comes running, and, when he's trodden my hen, I pull her back by the string, pues."

Meanwhile, by the sale of the eggs and a chick that she

thought might not, after all, be a pullet, she acquired two ducks.

Then one night a marauding tlacuache killed two of my hens. Candelaria was frantic. Immediately after dishing up the supper, she armed herself with a large bucket and a heavy stone and scampered off down the huerta to hide behind a clump of poinsettias, past which, she said, when the moon rose, the opossum was sure to pass. And when later I went down to shut the beach gate, she was fast asleep on the ground with her feet on a straw mat.

"It was just as I told you, señor," she said the following morning. "When the moon came up, I woke and the animal returned to eat where he'd killed last night."

"And what did you do?"

"I caught him, of course."

"Yes, but how?"

"I put the bucket over his head," said Candelaria, as if it were the most natural thing in the world to do. "Then I threw the stone on top so that he couldn't escape, pues. And I've sold the skin to that Nieves for her little coat of furs."

But a few days later Candelaria came to me one morning in tears.

"My hen, señor, my poor hen! She has decomposed herself and won't put any more. She was trodden by a turkey cock. I threw her over the wall as usual with her little maize, and I didn't put myself ready. The turkey cock came running instead of the rooster, and he trod her. Do you know what I think? I think that Agapito did it on purpose, and it's all the fault of that Cayetano because he wouldn't sell him our charcoal slack for firing his bricks."

All morning she was recounting this misfortune to someone or other in the kitchen, and she got so worked up telling Don Braulio, the baker, about it that, although he has the name for never giving away so much as a crumb, he offered her a five-centavo sweet roll to compose her.

About the middle of the afternoon she recovered. The black and white hen had disappeared.

"I sold her, señor," said Candelaria casually. "I sold her and bought two more." And she almost winked, which I took to mean she had wrung a good bargain.

"Did you tell them that it wouldn't lay?"

"Naturally that not," said Candelaria scornfully. "Like that they wouldn't have given me a good price. I sold her to those Hungarians, the ones who were here before, in the season of the waters, they who stole the little weights from my scales and the flowers of the azaleas of bougainvillea."

I am sorry to say that the gypsies were not the only thieves in Ajijic. Ever since I had been here I had kept small change in my living room, in a wooden box which was known as the fortune.

"We needed flour and little peppercorns more than I had money for out of my daily," Candelaria would say, "and I took the little centavos out of the fortune."

Often, if I were out of doors, I sent one or other of the servants to take any small sum needed. I knew always roughly what was there, and if I had been robbed at all it was of such tiny amounts as to be inconsiderable. I did not think I had been robbed at all. But now suddenly the money started going, and not only the centavos. For a long time we did not have the fat silver pesos, but instead dirty little scraps of paper, and these peso bills were disappearing from the box too, that is, if there were three or less, none went, but if there were more they did. This is a country where you are incessantly paying for things in small quantities, and I did not want to have to go about all day with my trouser pockets laden with piles of coin and my shirt pockets bulging with one-peso bills. The pilferer might have been any one of the servants, but I took to counting exactly what I had left in the fortune, and observation of times and opportunities soon left little doubt that it was Obdulia who was mulcting me. Mexican servants will take such things as sugar, or a little bottleful of kerosene, or rare objects such as pins, but it is most unusual for them to take coins or bills. Obdulia, though a clod, was a good worker, and the whole thing was disagreeable. My evidence was purely circumstantial, and after consideration I called all the servants together, told them what was happening, and said it had better stop. It was a painful interview. Afterward, one by one, they sought me out.

Lola lumbered up with a child clinging to her skirts and gesturing with a very dirty dishrag.

"It is three weeks, señor, since I have so much as been inside your room, and then as you know it was to fetch that book with the picture of two bulls." She pushed the child away from her skirts, and it began to howl. "And if you suspect me, señor, you have only to tell me, and I go to my house. You will know."

Cayetano was in the sulks.

"Once, señor, and once only, I took a little peso for me from the fortune, when you were out and there came a man selling huaraches for eight pesos and I had only seven, and I at once told you as soon as you came back. It was the day the señor of the oven sent you some slices of bread, very black and sticky. It was that Obdulia."

But Obdulia's face wore its usual impenetrable blank.

"It is Nieves who does your room, señor," she said. "And I, look at my dress. If I had been taking money, would I not have bought a new one?"

Aurora came limping and whining.

"Of course, señor, I am the poorest, as everyone knows, and with all certainty you suspect me, especially since I only come to the house from time in when to bring the laundry or to inquire how you are, and the others will say it was I. I know who it was. It was Cayetano. But nobody will believe me, they will say I did it, and what can we do, pues?"

Nieves was in tears and almost unable to speak.

"Señor, señor, and you know that I send money to my brother who is studying to be a priest, but how could I steal and do that?"

Candelaria was outraged.

"Never, señor, never anywhere that I have worked, not with my compatriots, nor with foreign señores from Hamburg and Bordeaux and the Canada, have I ever been accused of dishonesty. And if you want to know who it was, it was Lola, and Aurora, and Obdulia, and Cayetano and Silvanito. And that Nieves."

The incident was unpleasant, and I was still both hurt and cross when I told Mrs. Fountanney about it. I think I told her because she was about the only person who hadn't tried to run my household for me. She listened with her tortoise lids lowered as she stitched at her embroidery.

"Don't let it get you down," she said as her needle painted a coral-pink band below the faded smoke grays. "You know, when one doesn't have them any longer, there's nothing one misses so much as the little things that irritated one."

Just then an old and unfruitful nut tree at the edge of the huerta burst into flame. It was dry and sapless and went up like a torch. I saw Silvanito retreating from the conflagration, and called to him.

"Did you do that?"

"Yes, señor."

"What ever for?"

"There was a snake up there, pues, with a nest."

"What kind of snake?"

"A tilcuate. Big, with a body thick like this, like your wrist, and long of a meter or a meter and a half and black, and they make nests in trees and run after people."

"Why did you set fire to the tree? It wasn't much good, but it made some shade."

"I couldn't reach the nest. And, señor—"

He stopped and plaited his fingers and a deep red came up under his tawny skin.

"Well?"

"The other day, I think it was Tuesday—it is Tuesday that comes after Monday, isn't it?—I took sixteen centavos from the fortune, and fifteen I spent in a pencil at Doña Arcelia's. It pains me much, and I tell you that you may punish me."

There was a little pause.

"But I have gotten rid of the snake," he said proudly.

"Will the fire have killed it, or will it just have driven it down from the tree?" I asked.

"Who knows?" said Silvanito. "When are you going to castigate me?"

Although there were no further thefts from the fortune, the whole episode had left an unpleasant taste, and what with this and the imminent loss of Candelaria I found myself fretting. The time for her departure finally approached, and daily, alternately smiling and weeping, she cooked longer, more elaborate, and more delicious meals, as if determined to make us miss her. I had interviewed several local girls with a view to replacing her, without finding anyone satisfactory, and I even advertised in Guadalajara, receiving only one reply, from a pert young girl with magenta lips who claimed to have been to a school of cookery in Mexico City, asked three times the normal wages and, judging by the practiced but uncouth play of her button-like eyes, would undoubtedly want to make herself at home in parts of the house other than the kitchen. I was getting really worried when, two mornings before Candelaria's proposed departure, as I was sitting on the terrace there came a shuffling, followed by a sigh and a small whining voice. Aurora was standing at my elbow with a bundle of washing and a girl I'd never seen before.

"This is Apolonia, señor," she said. "I met her by chance down the street. She has left a post in Guadalajara, a post in the house of elegant gentry, very exigent. She is a cook."

It was a relief. I talked to the girl, and in the end she promised to come for a few weeks, starting the next day so as to find her way about before Candelaria left.

All morning there were two cooks in the kitchen, and all morning they both talked at once. It was one o'clock when

Candelaria discovered that she was behindhand with lunch, indeed that practically there was no lunch. She burst into tears, and before she had mopped them up with her apron, Apolonia had taken over. She worked very calmly. It turned out that she did everything with the utmost composure, but the lunch though not very late was only tolerable.

The next morning, which was Candelaria's last, she woke me up at six o'clock.

"Señor, señor! Doña Chabela is going to Guadalajara, and she is here, and she wants something to take many eggs in, and she is taking the big tin breadbox."

I told Candelaria to say that I was sorry that we needed the breadbox but that there were a number of cartons at her disposal.

"But how can I?"

"Why not? It's not at all a rude message."

"That no. But she isn't here."

"I thought you said she was."

"Yes, she was. But she's gone."

"Then what about the breadbox?"

"She took it, pues."

I think I just stared at Candelaria, dazed.

"Oh, I've sent Silvanito to catch the bus," she said. "With a carton."

A little later Silvanito came panting, clasping the big breadbox, which he put on my bed. He had easily overtaken the bus, which was having a wheel changed two minutes after starting.

"And Doña Chabela says that she only took the breadbox because it was not eggs but little chicks, and she thought the little holes for air would benefit them on the journey. But we made holes in the carton, with a big thorn."

After that beginning the day continued in a state of excitement. Candelaria was collecting her belongings, which included an old bamboo cage containing a drab brown bird, which on rare occasions sang very sweetly, and a new bamboo cage full of clothes. She was not leaving by bus. She had made an arrangement with a canoa that would be returning from Chapala to take her down the lake to San Pedrito, where the Mexico City highway passes, and where she could pick up a bus for Jiquilpan. She was in a great state as to whether the canoa would arrive or not. She was forever popping up to the roof, and half a dozen times she saw a canoa, but each time it was the wrong one and sailed straight past Ajijic.

"If that Carmen doesn't come with his canoa," she said, "it will all be the fault of Don Braulio, who said Carmen would come and who did not give me at all a good price for my poultry. And I meant to say, Don Braulio's bread has been very bad recently, and I told him he should be shamed, for even the Señor of the Oven makes a bread less bad."

At last, in the afternoon, the right canoa arrived and put in. It was already carrying a big bed. The frame, strung with thongs, was lodged across the stern, projecting at the sides, and the ends were propped upright in the prow. Tied to the frame were a pair of geese.

All the servants came down to see Candelaria off; so did the Professor, and he made the boatman arrange Candelaria's things three separate times, according to some scientific theory of the disposal of cargo. When it was all done the second boatman arrived with two sacks of charcoal and plumped them in the bows. The Professor sighed.

"Now it's all wrong again," he said. "Oh, dear."

Pushing back his hat, he mopped his brow and gave up.

At last Candelaria herself climbed in, clutching the cage with the songbird, and settled on a narrow thwart below the bed frame and above the geese. There was a pause while one of the boatmen had a long shouted conversation with a fisherman friend two hundred yards away, and then suddenly the canoa cast off. With tears pouring down her face, her arms waving and the bird cage waving too, Candelaria screamed farewells. The geese honked. And very slowly the canoa was poled out. In about five minutes they started to put up the sail, and at one moment it seemed that Candelaria and the bed must have been swept overboard by it. But suddenly she popped up the other side of the sail, still gesticulating. There was a brisk breeze, the sail filled quickly, and the canoa was soon spinning off. As long as I could see her, Candelaria was waving her arms, and the bird cage.

I had decided to keep Apolonia. A recommendation from Aurora wasn't encouraging, but I was in no position to pick and choose. She seemed agreeable—a plain, plump, walnut-colored girl in her early thirties, I judged, and she had a willing smile.

"Oh, yes," she had said when I interviewed her, "I know to cook many things. You see, I have worked in the city, and there I learned to cook an octopus in its ink."

Many Indios will tell you they have worked in the city. They seem to think it gives them a diploma for whatever job they are applying for at the moment. Apolonia claimed to be able to do almost everything, and when I showed her the kitchen she gave the floor a severe glance, and said, "Very dirty. Every day, after midday in the afternoon, I shall sweep it with coffee grounds. I know about floors. And I was wondering, señor, if you wouldn't give me permission now to go down to the beach? I would like to wash my hair in the lake."

I soon found she wasn't a very good cook. She was punctual, which pleased the Professor, and she served things hot, which is always a problem for foreigners in Mexico. But she could make only a few dishes and these all Mexican, and she put chili and coriander into everything. She appeared to spend very little time in her kitchen because she was always doing something else, and wherever she was she sang in a tuneless, clattering voice or chewed bubble gum.

"What ever are you doing now?" I said, seeing her one day seated in the huerta picking apart a mattress.

"There was a bedbug, señor," she said. "So I thought I'd throw a hand to remaking it while waiting for my ollas to boil. I know about mattresses, pues."

A lot of people come down to Mexico and talk as if there

weren't such a thing as a bedbug in the whole United States. Perhaps they are more noticeable in Mexico, just as in Spain the slums are more noticeable, because they always open right off the main street. And it is true that bedbugs may invade the best-kept houses or new houses. You may have them in the first six months or you may live free of them for twenty years and then suddenly acquire them. But look at the hovels your servants come from and you will see that bedbugs will be liable to occur anywhere until the general standard of living is raised, from the bottom upward. In warm climates bedbugs breed rapidly, and you must watch out. But if you have your bedding aired and the bed disinfected once a week, you oughtn't to be troubled. I have the beds sprayed with Formol or DDT. Or a fifty-fifty mixture of ammonia and turpentine will keep the bedbugs away, but it will probably keep you away too.

31.

CAYETANO told me one evening that Venustiano was ill. I went round to see him and found him in bed in the alcove of the one room of his adobe house. It was late, and the only lights were a smoking kerosene lamp and a candle stuck in a bottle and a tiny flame burning before a big picture of Our Lady of Zapopan. His nieces were sitting chattering on the veranda, and his wife, a good but invincibly stupid woman, was hovering about doing nothing.

I took his temperature. It was a hundred and two. The wrinkled skin of his forehead felt like hot paper. His breathing came chokingly. He was drowsy and dropped off to a half sleep every few minutes, but as soon as he woke, you could see how he resented his helplessness. He was taking, as usual, tisanes prepared by his wife.

"He won't even have an aspirin," said one of the nieces.

Living in an isolated village with no resident doctor, I am used to injecting myself, and I urged Venustiano to let me give him some penicillin. But he wouldn't hear of it.

The next day he was worse. His fever had gone down a little in the morning, but by the afternoon it was soaring higher than ever, and the mucus was bubbling in his chest.

"Yes, he is worse," said his wife, "but this morning I managed to persuade him to make a little vow to the Virgin, nothing difficult, though, as you know, he doesn't give importance to those things. So, though he is worse, he will be better."

Venustiano had been asleep when I arrived. But he then opened his eyes amid their mesh of wrinkles. He was not at all delirious.

"Look, Venustiano," I said. "Your wife tells me you've taken a vow—you! Now if you've done that, which you know you don't believe in, to please her, why won't you take some penicillin, which you don't believe in either, to please me? Surely that is what a reasonable man would do."

Venustiano looked at me with the expression of a grown-up allowing a couple of kids to trick him.

"What a man has to suffer when he's sick," he said. "Every three hours, you say? And how do I wake up that often?"

"I'll see to that."

I gave him his injection and went home to supper. I told the Fountanneys about Venustiano.

"You're going to sit up all night injecting him?" said the Professor.

"Well, they haven't a clock, and his wife's not capable of injecting him, even, if they had."

Mrs. Fountanney glanced at me under the brows that made her look so supercilious.

"You'll be a wreck. I shall come at two o'clock and relieve you. Don't be silly, Logan. I can sleep all day tomorrow if I want to. And I know where the house is, and I'm not in the least afraid of going there alone at night. No, I mean it. I shall be there."

And she was. Punctually at two o'clock she knocked at the door. She had a thermos and her embroidery and a little battery lamp shaped like a lantern, which gave a smooth white light. The nieces and Venustiano were asleep, but his wife set up a great whispered to-do about the señora. Mrs. Fountanney established herself at once where she could see Venustiano and enjoy the light without its disturbing him.

"You can be quite at ease," she told me, "so go home and get some sleep. After the eight-o'clock dose I shall return for breakfast."

I looked back at her as I went out of the door. She had already put on her big glasses and was straightening her canvas. Everything about her was as different from everything about Venustiano's wife as it could be, and the few things she had brought were conspicuous among Venustiano's possessions. Yet she did not look in the least out of place, any more than Venustiano looked out of place in my armchair when he came to call. I realized that she had exactly the same calm dignity as Venustiano himself and that neither of them would ever take on the color of their surroundings or be out of place anywhere in the world.

Just as I was preparing to go round to Venustiano's the next morning, Nieves came to say that Señora de los Bohorques would like to speak to me.

I found the old lady pacing up and down her room, obviously very agitated. I had half expected she wanted to complain about the noise of a party that some of my guests had held the night before, but she at once told me that she must leave the next day and that she hoped I would not interpret this abrupt departure as dissatisfaction with anything in my so agreeable house.

"I have had a letter from my niece, señor, my favorite niece, who was orphaned and whom I brought up. Unfortunately she made a marriage that turned out unhappy, and for many years she has been separated from her husband. And now she writes to say that she has fallen in love and wants a divorce in order to marry again."

She stopped and paced again, running her beautiful hand over her brow.

"You know, of course, señor, that our church does not recognize divorce. But that would be the least, since for the church a civil divorce simply does not exist. But to marry again! So you see, it is imperative that I should go to advise her what is right."

I gave way to my curiosity and asked what she would advise.

"Señor, she has been unhappy. She has not had anything of her life. She is not a girl, and perhaps she has found something of true happiness. One is not inhuman. And if it is indeed so, then she must take him as a lover, for so long as she does not commit such an outrage as marrying after a divorce I can continue to receive her. And I shall go on foot next week with the pilgrimage to Talpa in order that Our Lady may guide my niece aright."

32.

SOME other Mexican friends of mine who had been on the pilgrimage to Talpa found themselves benighted in a small village where all available accommodation had already been taken by other pilgrims. After a long search they found a bakery, and in the bakery were some benches and a huge oven with some shelves in it. Eleven of them of assorted ages and sexes spent the night on the benches and shelves. But this was not the point of the anecdote; such a thing might happen to anybody in Mexico. What had perturbed them was that the bakery was not equipped with chamber pots. So they went out, and, finding no chamber pots, bought half a dozen earthenware ollas for the exigencies of the night.

Chamber pots are ubiquitous in Mexico. And Mexican servants do not put them back in the bedrooms after doing the rooms. "I shall leave them out in the huerta to sweeten themselves in the sun," says Nieves. And then Cayetano borrows one of them to water the zinnia seedlings with, and a mason borrows another to fetch a little sand from the beach for mixing his mortar. But often they do not get as far as the huerta but are left in piles in any odd corner of the patio, and no other article of furniture is more in evidence. Then, in the evening, when turning down the beds, Nieves puts back the pots. If, as is quite likely, I am sitting in the patio with visitors, she passes through the group carrying a pot proudly before her, as if it were a challenge cup she had just won.

In the stores in Guadalajara you can buy chamber pots of all shapes and sizes, in any material, at all prices, and I always seem to be buying new ones for the house or paying Homobono to solder them. Homobono is a tinker, and he calls at the house every few months. His back wears a big hump, his legs are short and sturdy, and his arms very long and thin. His cheeks fall into crooked puckers, and he is full of fun. Slung over his shoulder on a leather strap is a square wooden box that holds his tinker's kit. He asks for charcoal, and he charges very low prices for his work. All the women come out with their broken metalware when he passes through the village, and they all have smiles for him, and he has chuckles and a pert phrase for all of them. Nothing he mends stays mended for very long, but maybe that is deliberate so that he can mend it again. He spends all his life on the road. The last time he came, he had just finished soldering a watering can and some sauce pans when Nieves came running along with a chamber pot.

"Look," she said. "It has a little puncture here, and another one over here."

Homobono took the pot and looked at it professionally from under his heavy lids.

"It's had a long life," he said with a chuckle. "Allah grant it's been a merry one."

He cleaned the rusted edges of the holes, pursing up his mouth and humming to himself. Then he cut some patches out of an old scrap of metal and began to solder them over the holes, carefully smoothing them with his iron.

"There," he said. "Now it's as fresh as a widow with a new husband."

But it was really past mending, and in order to stop Nieves putting it back in the room I told her to throw it away.

"That would give me much pain," she said.

Of course, there comes a moment in the life of any chamber pot when it no longer serves the purpose for which it was made, but in Mexico that does not mean you throw it away. When later I went to the kitchen, there just outside the door was the pot with several sickly geranium cuttings in it.

"The little holes will soon come undone," said Apolonia, "and like that the water will drain, and the little blooms will render better. I know about flowers, pues, and did you say I was to lard the meat with teeth of garlic instead of chili?"

"Yes, garlic. No chili."

"There isn't any garlic."

"Yes, there is, pues," said Nieves darting forward. "In this box, where we always keep them."

I have found that a good way to deal with a piece of tough village meat is to put it into a heavy iron pot, with half a dozen tomatoes, a few sweet peppers, a large onion, bay leaves, a little fat, and half a cup of red wine and let it simmer all the morning, adding some finely crumbled pumpernickel to the liquid a few minutes before serving.

"When it's cooked," I said, "I want you to serve it surrounded with all the vegetables in that big casserole I bought in Guadalajara."

It is difficult to get large earthenware dishes with proper handles in Mexico, and you are forever burning your fingers. After months of searching I had found one in the back of a dusty stall in the market of San Juan de Dios.

"Oh, no, señor," said Apolonia. "Not in that."

"But this is just the sort of thing I bought it for."

"But Doña Chabela is coming to lunch," said Nieves.

"Exactly."

"You couldn't serve a señora from that dish, pues," said Apolonia, popping her gum.

"Why ever not?"

Apolonia looked at Nieves, and they both giggled.

"It's a chamber pot, pues," said Nieves, blushing scarlet and rushing out of the room.

"Well, I didn't know that, Apolonia," I said. "But I don't see that it really matters; it's never been used as one, and it's perfectly clean."

"Oh, no, señor," she said. "It wouldn't serve to hand to a señora. You see, I know about chamber pots. It's a woman's chamber pot, posen."

33.

"SEÑOR," said Cayetano, pointing to the row of eucalyptus trees that border my land, "we must cut all the branches overhanging the road or we shall be fined."

"Why?"

"Because the Señor Inspector of Roads is coming to the village tomorrow."

All over Ajijic people were lopping and trimming their trees. Machetes of all ages, shapes, and sizes were pressed into service, owners of saws did a brisk business hiring them out, and nimble small boys were everywhere in great demand as tree climbers. The miller wrote a notice on his blackboard in red chalk, saying that he would grind corn free for one week for the family that would undertake to trim his mango trees. Then suddenly all activity stopped.

"What ever shall we do, señor?" said Cayetano. "They say that, with the Señor Inspector of Roads, is also coming the Señor Inspector of Forests, who will fine us for cutting the trees. In many parts of the village they have already cut their trees, but what shall we do, pues?"

"But you can't be fined just for chopping off some branches," I said. "They do it everywhere, to make stakes and posts."

"That yes no, señor. They don't cut off main branches; only someone very closely related to the señor inspector can do that; and once he even fined a compadre with whom he was quarreled."

"Well, what constitutes a main branch?"

Cayetano thought about this for a moment.

"Any big branch, señor, that is to say, any branch that isn't a little branch."

This sounded like a racket, and I went round to see Venustiano, now recuperating, to ask him what to do. I found him in the street outside his house sitting very upright in a backless wooden chair.

"Maybe they won't animate themselves to arrive after all," he said. "But who knows."

"What are you going to do?"

Venustiano considered me for a moment, and then he smiled in the way he does when he is wondering how completely he is going to answer my question.

"I?" he said. "I'm not going to do anything. I know these people. Once, many years ago, they used the same trick. They made a lot of money in a village over there where the uncle of my cousin was living. He was the only man in the whole village they couldn't fine."

"How did he manage?"

"My cousin's uncle was always very ready," said Venustiano. "There were three big guava trees growing just inside the dry wall surrounding his yard, and many of the branches hung right over the wall into the street. Apart from not having any money to pay a fine, he didn't want to cut the branches and lose so much of the crop, for both he and his wife were very fond of guavas, though she liked quinces slightly better."

Venustiano paused. He had been sweating, and he wiped his face carefully on his sarape.

"What did he do?" I asked.

"He moved the dry wall, pues, and that is very hard work, as I can tell you. He moved it in, so that the three trees were just outside the wall, in the roadway."

"But then I should have thought that the Inspector of Roads would have had the whole trees cut down."

"Oh, no," said Venustiano. "The Inspector of Reafforestation was there too, and he wouldn't have allowed that. You see, they were only just outside the wall. Look, like those two trees there."

I followed Venustiano's eye along the road to where two pomegranates appeared to be growing just outside the dry wall surrounding his land. I noticed the loosely laid stones where the wall curved inward around the trees, and that there was plenty of earth scattered about.

"But of course," added Venustiano, "one can always pay the inspectors five pesos not to call at your house at all, if you have five pesos, that is, though I expect they'd charge you more."

But I decided I wouldn't pay anybody anything. I wanted to see if it were possible just to obey the law and not be fined. I went round my land carefully with Cayetano and pointed out to him which branches to lop and which not. It took most of the afternoon, but by the end of it I was satisfied that neither inspector could have any genuine grounds for fining me.

"And now," said Cayetano, proudly viewing the work, "at all places where we cut the branches I'll cover the wounds with mud so that they won't show."

"There's no need to do that," I said. "We haven't cut any main branches."

"You will know, señor," said Cayetano. "The Señores Inspectors will be here tomorrow."

But they didn't come the next day. Or the next. Or the day after that. We heard they were still in Chapala, drunk. They had started out from Guadalajara with a flurry of efficiency and had collected a lot of money from the villages on their way to Chapala. They had even fined the priest in Ixtlahuacán. Some said that they had fallen out in Chapala over the division of the proceeds, while others said they were just staying there a few days to untire themselves.

A week later the Inspector of Roads passed through Ajijic on his way to Jocotepec. He didn't stop in the village at all. But the same day, a little before lunchtime, the Inspector of Reafforestation called at my house.

He was a small round man, very genial, and every time he opened his mouth to speak a gold tooth flashed in the sunlight. He seemed interested in his job and was very well informed. I walked round my land with him, and he expressed himself entirely satisfied with what I had done and was able to give me some good advice about grafting grapefruit onto citron.

"I only wish others would care for their trees as you do," he said. "But these of here are just like so many mules without heads. Why, you must have doubled the value of your property already. How much do you consider it to be worth now?"

We had a little glass of tequila together in the patio, and before he left he fined me ten pesos for destroying the nut tree that Silvanito had burned in order to kill the tilcuate.

34.

FOUR unusual guests arrived and left within a week. The first to come was a Miss Dodwell, an Englishwoman of what the Professor gallantly described as uncertain age, for, though she had glittering golden hair, she was seventy if she was a day. She arrived alone in a station wagon piled with luggage, and I put her in the room next to Fordyce.

Directly after lunch she went out to inspect the huerta, set up an easel a few yards from where Cayetano was working and began to paint and to chatter in pidgin Spanish. Presently, from the roof terrace where I was working, I saw Cayetano, rather pink, making for the tool shed, but five minutes later the chatter was resumed, and there was Silvanito holding her brushes. He, too, looked very ill at ease.

At cocktail time she was the life and soul of the party, though it was clear after the first drink—and Miss Dodwell did not confine herself to one—that any man within winking distance was fair game to her. Halfway through supper she said I looked lonely at my table, picked up her glass, and came and sat beside me, holding my hand throughout the rest of the meal.

Later she proposed bridge. She ordered a double brandy and insisted on partnering the Professor, but by now her gaiety was such that she would bid nothing but hearts. Rather unsurprisingly, her luck at cards was astonishing and in spite of her eccentricity the game was prolonged. Finally, however, Mrs. Fountanney made a small slam.

"Rubber!" cried Miss Dodwell and fell flat on her face.

Professor Fountanney and I carried her to her room. As we laid her on the sofa a strand of hair caught in the Professor's glasses, and her whole coiffure fell to the floor. Miss Dodwell was bald as a coot.

I don't know what occurred during the night, but in the morning Fordyce, who never appears normally until lunchtime, tackled me at the breakfast table.

"Look here," he said. "Either that floozie goes or I go."

That was that. At midday Miss Dodwell departed in her station wagon for the Nido Hotel in Chapala. Fun though she was, I had other guests to consider and felt obliged to tell her that her room was booked.

As a matter of fact a guest did arrive that evening. An Episcopalian minister from Oregon, and clearly rich, he adopted a democratic manner with us all and announced that he had come to Mexico in order, as he put it, to give his parishioners a holiday for a few months. Every morning he bathed in the lake before breakfast, and on Sundays he walked up the mountain to sing his favorite hymns, standing alone in a deep gully high above the Eye of Water. For a visitor in a Latin country he was very outspoken about the Catholic Church, and the general trend of his talk was such that I was not surprised when, after a day or two, I heard him ask the Professor what he thought about the Great Russian Experiment. Professor Fountanney regarded him for a moment.

"When I was a boy," he said, "my friends' experiments, as they called them, usually filled the house with very unpleasant smells. That is, if they failed to blow anything up."

Everyone laughed, but the minister was not amused, and the next morning he, too, packed his bags and left to join Miss Dodwell at the Nido—just in time to miss the arrival of the Princess in Ajijic.

The Princess was bleached, with upswept hair, a beautiful make-up, an excellent figure, and simple, expensive clothes. The man had curly brown hair, a curly brown beard, and he wore sandals and a Hawaiian printed shirt.

"At anything under fifty yards," as somebody who had spotted them in Guadalajara afterward observed, "it was obvious that he was twenty years younger than she. A beard doesn't really age a man, but old women with young lovers always seem to think it does."

As I came into the patio, the young man rose, standing a little way behind the woman's chair, and the woman smiled. Her appearance was as artificial as that of a porcelain figurine, but she had charm, and it was natural charm.

"Good morning, is this an awkward time to arrive?" she said, and though the intonation of her voice was cosmopolitan, it had a Middle Western timbre. "We heard about this lovely place in Guadalajara. I am the Princesse de Lamballe. We should like a room."

They looked a little above my standards, but I showed them round, and they chose the corner room that had two big windows. I saw the woman look quickly at the door of the closet to see if there were another door, leading to a bathroom. There wasn't, but she didn't say anything. I told them I'd have their luggage sent along.

"Here are the keys of the rumble," said the young man, who was clearly not the Prince de Lamballe. He looked shy.

"Lamballe?" said the Professor doubtfully. "I thought that title was extinct. The house of Elbeuf, I believe. Maybe a cadet branch—perhaps she's divorced."

However, she was not the first woman to hang onto a title, whether spurious or genuine, or to have a young lover, and it was none of it any business of mine. I hoped their visit would pass quietly. But, without doing anything but behave naturally and nicely, they disrupted the entire household. I tried not once but many times to tell the servants, jointly and severally, that it was impolite to stare. But in vain. They were so eminently stareworthy, the Princess and the young man. There was nothing at all about them that was ordinary, that conformed to any standard that Ajijic had ever heard of. Cayetano, offering the Professor the soup, went into a trance with his head slewed round, gazing at the other table. Lola fell up the steps, her eyes boring into the young man. Silvanito simply anchored himself as near as possible to where they were sitting and set a world's record in time passed without blinking. Nieves took an unparalleled time fixing their room and came out bubbling with inside titbits.

"She's done nicely for herself, but it doesn't seem just, with so many pretty young women about," said Lola, and the eyes glittered in her fat brown cheeks.

The Professor, surprisingly enough, was a little overawed. He always looked away when either of them came out of the room the whole household knew they were sharing, but when they were not looking, he stared at them almost as hard as the servants did. Perhaps his time sense was outraged for the Princess looked, in spite of her modern dress, rather as if she had been preserved under glass at the Petit Trianon, a delicate piece of biscuit de Sèvres that would break at a touch. Mrs. Fountanney treated them as she did everybody else, and one evening she took them to play poker with Mr. Humpel. I found them both polite, appreciative of what there was, and with enough sense not to ask for things that there obviously weren't.

The staring household they could, I think, have overlooked, but the staring village proved too much for them. When they went for a walk on the beach, everyone stared; children followed them about, and if they sat down anywhere, adults gradually collected around them, silent and intent. So they, too, followed the minister and Miss Dodwell down to the Nido.

I asked Venustiano what it was about them that made the village stare, but he couldn't or wouldn't tell me.

"Yes, all the fools are chattering about them," he said, "but they didn't draw my attention. The beard of a man and the blouse of a woman—"

35.

"I HAVE six years and my mama says if you don't want to buy these eggs, and will you please put the centavos in this handkerchief and make a big knot such as I can't undo and spend them?"

Since this breathless sentence of his first visit Mateo has only spoken to me once again. He comes twice a week. His lips are buttoned, and his face assumes a worried scowl while I am counting the eggs out of his little yellow wicker basket. I believe he thinks that if I drop one he will somehow be to blame, for the moment I have finished he smiles. His apple-pink face gets plumper and pinker, and his smile broadens and deepens until his face is no longer big enough to contain it and it overflows. But he never speaks.

The servants say he never speaks to them. He opens the door, peers inside for a moment, and walks through the patio and on into the living room or wherever I happen to be. He will go all over the house until he finds me. The dogs don't like him. They charge him, baying like a pack, but he doesn't seem to mind. He holds his miniature sarape up to his face and stands perfectly still while they bark and sniff all round him, and then he advances slowly to where I am sitting, holding the basket of eggs out in one hand and the handkerchief for the centavos in the other.

One morning Mateo's mother brought him to me with a deep cut on his knee.

"He was playing and fell and did this," she said. She told me the name of the child with whom he'd been playing when the accident happened, the name of the child's father, on which side of the street he had fallen, and whose fault it was. And then, from the folds of her rebozo, she produced a bloodstained stone. "And this," she said, "is what he fell on."

Mateo never said a word.

I washed the wound, and then I went to fetch the alcohol.

"Mateo," I said, "this is going to hurt you, but only for a moment."

Mateo continued to look at the ground, keeping his leg rigidly in the position I had put it. He squirmed a little, and the tears began to pour down his face. But he never made a sound. And when I gave him a piece of candy, he spread out a clean handkerchief on the floor and put the candy in it for his mother to tie a big knot.

"He is a good boy," his mother said. "He doesn't give war."

Indio children don't give war. They are very self-contained, and if they cannot find a friend to play with, they will play by themselves for hours, making their own primitive toys out of leaves and sticks. I made a top with a match and a Coca-Cola cap, and Mateo spun it tirelessly while I talked with his mother. Since then I have seen Coca-Cola caps spinning all over the village.

In the afternoon Mateo appeared again. This time he came with eggs. I counted them and asked about his leg. He smiled and held it up for me to see. But when I gave him the money for the eggs, the worried scowl returned; he looked at me uncertainly for a moment and toddled away without the money. In the doorway he turned and spoke.

"I go and come," he said.

He had forgotten to bring the handkerchief.

36.

CAYETANO appeared in my room, wearing a wide leather belt stretched tightly round his chest.

"Several months ago, señor, when I was carrying sacks of cement for the henhouse, I felt the pain. It has not left me, and now it is much."

I suggested he see a doctor.

"There's a señor here in the village who knows how to compose this," said Cayetano. "I went to him, and he said, yes, I was open in the chest."

"What does that mean?"

"It is what happens when you strain yourself. And I want to go to him that he may compose me, so can I have the morning off? And I was wondering, señor, if you didn't have a little bottle, because I want to buy some cooking oil?"

"What d'you want cooking oil for?"

"That is what he uses, pues. He puts it on the chest, all over the body, rubbing like this, until all the bones click into place and then I am composed."

So we had a manipulative surgeon in Ajijic. And the report on his practice showed him to be intelligent. In the afternoon Cayetano appeared again. He still wore the strap and was carrying half a dozen whitefish strung on a willow branch.

"He massaged and rubbed, señor, until my bones thundered, and I was open of the head, and of the chest, and of the back, here high, and here low down. And all my bones cracked and roared like thunder, down in my feet and legs too, for I was open there as well, and he made me bend my legs, and I must lie down today, and after tomorrow I go to him again, and I said I had to go to Chapala carrying things, and he said that would not harm me if I wore my belt like this, but that to-morrow I should not work, so I must work on Sunday instead."

"And how much is all this going to cost, Cayetano?"

"I do not know, señor, but it will be little, for d'you know who it is? It's that Guadalupe Paz to whom you lend money. And he says to say that he has a piece of land there by his house, left him by his aunt, and he mortgaged it for thirty pesos, and he has all the papers, but the man to whom he mortgaged it won't let him put his animals there, though Lupe clearly has the right, and he would pass the land to you for little or for nothing, for then the man would have to go, and he could put his animals back there. And he gives you these whitefish, señor, as a present."

"How nice."

"And he sends to say that now is due the repayment of the loan he owes us—ten pesos, would it be?"

I said nothing, and it irked Cayetano, who likes to know the amount of others' indebtedness, especially when he himself is in funds.

"He can't throw a hand to the centavos in effective, but he offers to sell us a thousand bricks at the price of San Antonio, some of which he will give us."

"Well, bricks cost fifty pesos a thousand now, so he can give me two hundred if he likes."

Cayetano considered this for a moment. Then, "How much would that be, pues?"

"The amount of the loan. Now you can work out how much he owes."

"But he wants to sell a thousand."

"I don't want a thousand. I'm buying bricks from Julián Ybarra and he hasn't finished delivering yet—"

"I forgot to say, señor," interrupted Cayetano, "Julián Ybarra says that now he doesn't want to make any more."

"Well, are Guadalupe's bricks any good?"

"Equal of good," said Cayetano, "to those of Julián. You wouldn't know the difference. You see, they're very closely related, and d'you know, I think they arranged themselves together about the bricks."

Professor Fountanney did not like Cayetano. Though he wanted quite a lot of service, he was always annoyed because Cayetano spent so much time sitting about doing nothing. But here, where so many errands have to be run, where there are no telephones, it had seemed to me a convenience to have a servant always on call to run and buy a box of matches, to take a note, to fetch a glass. And since I have no bells in the house that servant must be in a prominent place, easily called. Mrs. Fountanney would certainly have missed Cayetano, for she is one of those people who settle themselves in an armchair with an extensive equipment of books, needlework, and so on, and who invariably have forgotten one knitting needle, or the magazine with the article they are in the midst of reading, or the sock for which they have brought all the darning materials. I explained all this to the Professor.

"Personally, I like to go on these little errands myself," he said. "Get to know the village."

"Yes, but many people don't want to."

"Much better have a cowbell. I don't in the least mind buying one for myself."

But the thought of my guests wandering round with cowbells and occasionally no doubt sounding a simultaneous carillon was unattractive, and besides, I had an idea that, were no servant about, I would find myself more than ever the recipient of all requests. However, the Professor bought a cowbell, and he would thrust his arm outside his door and ring it mournfully for Cayetano, who was sitting three yards away. And when he went in to meals, he took the cowbell with him.

I doubt whether it would have been possible to give Professor Fountanney the immediate service he liked in the dining room, unless by allotting to him alone two servants so that there would always be one at hand, and that he would not have cared for since he was always saying he didn't like being watched at table.

It was quite remarkable how often he wanted something just when both Cayetano and Nieves were out of the room, but now he had the bell. It was a metal cowbell with a deep, powerful, lugubrious note; it echoed like a foghorn under the brick roof, and it could be heard all over the huerta; it reverberated through the kitchen and made Apolonia cry "Dios de mi vida!" It boomed down by the vegetable beds, and when he heard it little Silvanito would cross himself. It had a note of doom. I think it gave everyone the jitters. And then one day it disappeared.

The hunt went on for days, but nowhere could the bell be found. Everyone searched like mad, but all the same there was a lightness about the house as though a cloud had been lifted. The Professor went seldom to Guadalajara, and you can't buy cowbells in Ajijic. Then I found the bell. It was in my room behind some books.

"Are you sure you've no idea where the bell got to?" I asked Cayetano.

"I don't know at all, señor," he said, but in such a manner that I was convinced he had hidden it.

I am afraid that I connived at the sequestration of the Professor's property. The bell had gotten on my nerves too; it was not really necessary, and as Mrs. Fountanney hadn't made the slightest effort to look for it, I felt sure she didn't much want it found. We went on without the bell, and Nieves and Cayetano waited on the Professor so efficiently that he had hardly any cause to complain.

Then one night I heard a curious sound outside in the huerta. We had lost a spade and a mattock, both left about by Silvanito, for Indios will leave any tool where they have been using it, and I am quite incapable of making an evening checkup of everything used during the day. I thought it might be a thief. From my window I saw shadows moving among the young orange trees. There were two forms. Now in Mexico you have a right to shoot at anyone who is trespassing on your land at night, and if you kill him, well that is his fault. However, such drastic measures did not appeal to me, and for all I knew the men were armed themselves. The dogs were fast asleep. As house watchers they are not up to much, and had I put them out it was ten to one that Tippet would have made friends with the intruders and Monk would have barked at a safe distance. Then my eye fell on the Professor's cowbell. I shone my flash out of the window and rang the bell, and its deep, minatory clang boomed out into the night like a tocsin, like the summons to the Last Day. In the beam of the light I saw two figures fleeing. I rang them over the wall.

"What do you think?" said Silvanito, in the morning. "Over there, where I left the hoe and the spoon for planting and the sprinkler for the can, I found this knife, and it doesn't belong to anybody here, and Lola says she heard a terrible noise in the night, a very big noise, and she is sure there was a fight, a very big fight, though she cannot see any blood on the ground anywhere, but Nieves said she heard the noise too, and it was the sort of noise the Devil makes, and he left the knife."

I took the knife to my room and gave orders that if anybody inquired for it he should be brought to me. Nobody came. But I had to give the Professor back his cowbell. Fortunately, within a few days, Fordyce threw it into the lake. At least, the bell disappeared, and both Cayetano and Lady Connemara said that they had seen him throw something into the lake from the end of the jetty. The Professor asked him about it.

"What bell?" said Fordyce.

37.

A MAN I had never seen before climbed over the dry wall, picked a papaya, and sat cross legged on the grass eating it, paring off long yellow shreds with his dagger. I stood and watched him. When he had finished he took off his sombrero to me, said adiós, and left.

I asked Cayetano who he was.

"Who knows, señor. Though it is certain he wasn't a thief, for he ate the little melon here in the garden where we could see him."

An Indio will sometimes do this. He will not pick from a tree with only a few fruits or from a huerta with only a few trees. And he will not pick more than he himself can eat right there on the spot.

"I expect he was a stranger, far from his village and hungry," said Cayetano. "But if he had taken the melon away with him to sell or eaten it outside where we couldn't see him, then we should have known him for a thief. And I was wondering, señor, if you know where the key is?"

"Which key?"

"The English key."

"Yes, you left it here last night. What do you want it for?"

"To fix the key."

"I don't understand. To fix what key?"

"The key on the veranda, señor."

"But I don't want a key there. Which key?"

"That yes no. The key you wanted me to fix on the veranda. I want the English key to fix that key, pues."

We went on like this for some time. In Spanish, apart from the key you use in a door, a wrench is a key, and a faucet is a key, and for some reason an adjustable wrench is called an English key.

"I want the big little English key that arranges itself," said Cayetano, getting pink in the face and shouting, "in order to collocate on the veranda the little key of water, like you said."

All the same, Spanish is one of the easiest languages in the world, and it has a rich vocabulary. Its grammar is straightforward, and what few exceptions there are mostly behave themselves nicely, according to the rules for exceptions. Every now and then the government starts a campaign against illiteracy, and, a year or two ago, an order went out that everybody who could read and write must either teach one person to do so or pay ten pesos for them to be taught by someone else. I had debated for a time whether I should try and teach Candelaria, but she quite plainly didn't want to learn and would have become deafer and deafer to my efforts.

Then one day Silvanito came to me carrying a sheet of paper and said doubtfully, "Señor, says my mother that it would please her much if I could learn to spell like you, and if you wouldn't teach me, pues. I've written to my aunt, the one who went away, about her duck that she left with us. You see, she died—the duck, I mean. And here's the letter."

Spanish is spelt phonetically, but a confusion arises between the letters *b* and *v*, which are nearly always pronounced identically. To distinguish them, Mexicans refer to *b* as the big one and to *v* as the little one.

In Silvanito's letter I came to the word *viaje*, which means a journey. It was incorrectly spelled, with a *b*.

"Now, Silvanito," I said. "How d'you spell *viaje*?"

"Who knows, señor."

"Come along, you know quite well. Just think carefully. Is it the little one or the big one?"

Silvanito thought for a very long time. Then he said, "Señor, it depends on the length of the journey."

38.

DOÑA Chabela had told me that Apolonia would make trouble for me with the other servants since she was a Communist. I asked Apolonia if it were true.

"That yes yes, señor," she said, dropping a spoon and smoothing the ruffles in her dress of watermelon pink. "When I was in the city I worked in an oil factory, and we were all Communists."

"Well, are you contented here?"

"How not."

"I thought perhaps you wouldn't like to work in a house like this."

"Why not, señor?"

Of course she hadn't any idea what communism was. She'd had a boy friend in the city who said he was a Communist, so she said she was one too. It had made a change. Many people will tell you the Communists are strong in Mexico. But there are not many big cities for communism to breed in, and there is still a lot of food. The Ajijic Indio without his plot of land is rare, and I have often pointed out to them how lucky they are to have so much room for their crops. "Oh, yes," they answer, "we can sow and plant whenever God gives us license. We have much room, much where." The Mexicans, even the humblest peons, have more freedom than they would enjoy in most other countries, and up to date they have certainly enjoyed free speech as well. Politics are still an excuse for a binge.

Lola, who didn't like Apolonia, waddled up while we were talking and occasionally waved a dishrag at her in disagreement. Suddenly Cayetano burst in.

"Señor! Señor! I come at the run. The bees have swarmed. They are over there by the little mango of Manila but on one of the new lemon trees, and they are so heavy that its little branches are weeping and the bees are angry and I have been stung. I beat an empty bucket with my machete like Doña Chabela told me and made much noise, but they stung me again and here I am."

I know nothing about bees. I told Cayetano to make a fire with dry eucalyptus leaves and smoke them.

"Señor," said Apolonia, the Communist, "señor, please forgive me that I should have the insolence as to be so impertinent as to dare to put myself against the current of your words, but it is not so. It is very easy. You must throw water."

She seized Cayetano's bee veil and disappeared off down the huerta. In less than half an hour she had the swarm neatly hived.

"I know about bees," she said to Lola.

And it was while Apolonia was with us that we were expecting the young sow to farrow. I had consulted gestation tables showing the earliest, average, and latest dates the young might be expected. Since this was the sow's first litter, we had ignored the earliest date. The average period passed. Nothing happened. The latest date passed. Still nothing happened. Some days later, Cayetano fetched Venustiano, who looked long and knowingly at the sow, and said, "Maybe yes, maybe no."

And then he went into a very long trance, shaking his head from time to time.

"No," he said finally, still gazing at the sow. "No, not this time."

"I agree," said Apolonia.

So I sent Cayetano to the butcher to find out what price the sow would fetch for pork. He returned at the double.

"Says Don Vicente he doesn't want to buy the sow just now, señor, but could you sell him some honey for his daughter's chickenpox? But he offers a hundred and fifteen pesos for the sow the month that enters."

"Very cheap," said Apolonia.

Just then Lola lumbered up again. She picked a handful of grass and threw it halfway across the sty. The sow naturally made for it, thus presenting to Lola her stern. A swift glance was enough.

"Do not sell the little sow, señor," she said. "She will have her creatures at the finish of the moon."

And Lola was right. At the finish of the moon there were eight marmalade-colored piglets.

"*I* know about pigs," she said to Apolonia.

I was dividing some violets, which are among the hardiest plants here, when Nieves came along with a fly swatter. This instrument she loves, and assassinates all sorts of things with it apart from flies. Once she killed a lizard.

"That Obdulia isn't coming tomorrow," she said. "There came a message from her father, and she went on the afternoon bus to her house, though I told her she should ask permission."

The expression on her fine-boned face indicated that she herself would never do such a thing.

Obdulia was away for two days. On the third day she suddenly appeared at my side and said brightly, "Now I've come."

"So I see. But what have you been doing?"

"My father sent for me because of the witch, pues."

"The witch?"

"Yes. She had bewitched a great many people, very wickedly and very badly, people in Ixtlahuacán—she was of there, the witch I mean."

I remembered having skimmed an article about it in the Guadalajara paper.

"But what has that got to do with you?"

"She had bewitched my mother's brother, with whom she'd had a lawsuit over a cow, and my cousin-sister's husband, with whom she was quarreled. So she was killed in Zapopan, pues, but it was thought better to burn her in Ixtlahuacán, where they have plenty of wheat straw that burns quickly and hotly—

it's good wheat round there—so they made a mound of straw, and they put her on it, and they burned her and I saw it."

"Oh, they didn't burn her alive?" I asked.

"No. That is, if witches die like people. Anyway, there she was burning away, and I could distinctly see the shape of her skull through the flames—it was just like those sugar skulls they sell in the market on the Day of the Dead. It looked small and perfect just as they do."

Lola and Cayetano appeared from somewhere and sidled up to us to listen.

"And then, suddenly, the witch gave a most dreadful scream."

"Are you sure it was the witch?"

"Oh, yes. I expect it was her soul, being snatched by the Devil. Or so somebody there said. Anyway, it was a great big screech. But that wasn't the worst."

"Because, you see, señor," interrupted Lola, who had obviously heard the tale a dozen times already, "there was a woman standing quite near Obdulia—Cointa her name is—let out a frightful yell too. And that was very bad."

"Because," explained Obdulia, "when a married woman suddenly yells like that when a witch approaches—"

"Dead or alive," put in Cayetano.

"You see, it means she's given her husband horns. Or so they say. Anyway, whether she'd cheated him or not, Cointa got beaten by her husband that night. He locked the door from the yard and chased her with a thick plank of wood, and I saw that too."

On the whole this is a law-abiding region. We have an occasional murder, usually motivated by jealousy and committed in drink, but we don't go in for things like witch burning. I asked Obdulia if she weren't afraid of the police.

Her face blankened.

"Oh, I never saw the witch, señor," she said.

"But I thought you said you saw her burn?"

Lola suddenly picked up her duster, and Cayetano went off down the huerta.

"I just saw the mound of wheat straw on fire," said Obdulia, "and they said the witch was in it. They said she had been killed in Zapopan, and they said she was dead there in the fire. But how should I know?"

I said nothing, and after a moment Obdulia went on, "There used to be a witch, or at least all the world said she was a witch. But she went away a long time ago, various weeks, and who knows if they really killed her, perhaps it was someone else."

I still said nothing.

"I just saw the wheat straw burning. Perhaps there wasn't any person in it. Perhaps they didn't kill anyone. Perhaps some of those boys made a dummy and set fire to the straw."

She twisted her rebozo.

"They said it was wheat straw, but who knows."

Suddenly she gave a high-pitched giggle.

"Anyhow, now she can't make disgusts any more! I go at a run to my broom!"

I never heard of any police action about the witch burning, and even if an investigation had been made I expect that everyone concerned would have been as uncooperative as Obdulia. In spite of her discretion, however, rumors got around Ajijic, and one day Rendel said in his great thunderous voice:

"My mozo Abundio swears your maid's a witch, the pudding-faced one. I think that's marvelous. Could I have her put a murrain on Connemara? Witch ditches bitch! Have a drink!"

Interlude: VOLCANO

39.

WHENEVER I can arrange to get away for a few days, I like to go off in the car and see a bit of the country. The Fountanneys had long wanted to take one of these trips with me, and a good opportunity seemed to present itself one week when the inn was almost empty. Mr. Humpel, when I asked him, said he did not at all mind being left alone.

"In my little house I am not depending," he said, "and I shall be very well here alone. I need only my room brought to order, and with the little Nieves I have a fine relationship."

I told him he shouldn't put it quite like that.

"Ah, it means another thing? Then with her I have a good connection."

So, on a bright, flustery morning the Fountanneys and I set off. I took Silvanito along, for it is often useful to have a little fetch-and-carry or someone to leave with the car so that your hub covers and valve caps aren't stolen. Besides I had the dogs with me, and Tippet needs a lot of watching. Though he brought no luggage, Silvanito had put on his best and cleanest clothes. His shirt, a little frayed at the edges, was ice-cream pink, he wore odd socks, and round his sombrero he had written his name with a blue pencil.

"Are you afraid of losing it?" I asked.

"Oh no. That's so that people may know I can write."

We drove down the lake toward Jocotepec, but it was not possible to enjoy much of the scenery because the Professor was battering me with questions.

"D'you mean to tell me," he asked, "that you haven't even a rough itinerary?"

"I've no plans at all, Professor. Whenever I see a side road I like the look of, I go along it."

This idea enchanted Mrs. Fountanney. Not so the Professor.

"Then you don't even know where we shall spend the night?"

"Exactly."

We drove in silence for a few minutes. Then, "Where are we making for after Jocotepec?"

"I don't know, Professor. Where would you like to make for?"

"No, it's your party," he said. "I don't want to butt in."

We stopped in Jocotepec, and we all went to see about a sarape I was having made. Professor Fountanney criticized the loom construction and the form of the bobbin; he found fault with the weave and the pattern of the half-finished sarape and said that the colored wools would not be fast. He felt very much better. But I knew he'd not be happy until he had some sort of schedule to keep us all up to, so I said to Mrs. Fountanney, "How would it be if we went along the lake to Jiquilpan to see if we can't find Candelaria? And then perhaps we could go up to Uruapan; I'd like to get some lacquer trays for the inn."

"That sounds very nice," she said.

"If you're going to Uruapan," said the Professor, "we can go to Paricutín."

"What ever for?" said his wife. "We've all seen it before."

The Professor said, "I would never allow a volcano to appear in any country I was in without investigating it thoroughly."

I believed him. And as the miles ran out against the dull blue glitter of the lake, he talked about every form of volcanic activity, from Krakatoa to the Valley of Ten Thousand Smokes. The little towns went by—San Luis Soyatlán, The place of the palms for plaiting, with the clumsy cement seats lining the plaza;

Tuxcueca, The place where they make petticoats of rabbit skin, with the white chapel on the green hillock; Tizapán, The place above a deposit of chalk, always unkempt and litter strewn. Then we turned away from the lake, winding over the hills above a series of alluvial valleys where crops grow like Jack's beanstalk and every level stretch is a patchwork of corn and sugar cane. Every time we stopped along the route Silvanito had some refreshment—now a paleta, which is a block of flavored water ice on a stick, now a length of sugar cane, now a glass of tamarind water. He gossiped everywhere and usually brought back a scrap of information or rumor.

"Here in this village," he observed, spitting sugar cane out of the car, "while the volcano the Señor Professor says we're going to see was small, the people were all very frightened and kept their children locked in their houses because it was said that trucks were going through the villages collecting children to throw into its fire, in order that it should not be very bad." He tore off another strip of sugar cane with his teeth. "I told them, pues, that nothing like that happened in Ajijic."

I had never heard of this kind of human sacrifice here, though Mexico has as bloody a history in this respect as any country in the world. The Aztecs offered thousands of victims to their war god, Huitzilopochtli, on whose altars, daily, steamed the hearts of scores of war captives. But then war was the Azteca's trade, and their very survival in the midst of numerous and more highly civilized rivals depended on their military prowess. Even the peace-loving Maya practiced human sacrifice, but in their isolated and parched limestone plain of Yucatán an assured water supply was a far more pressing need than any victory in battle, and so it was to the water god that they hurled the young virgins whose gold masks and slender bones have been brought to light in recent years from the bottom of the sacred well of Chichen Itzá. Among primitive peoples it seems that human offerings were made only to those gods who had to be placated at all costs, and though Mexico has always been subject to volcanic disturbance, her people have not labored under the ever present fear of sudden destruction, which has made, in other lands, a paramount deity of volcanic force. Mexico's volcanoes have elected to be dignified rather than destructive, and the stately giants that overhang the Valley of Mexico, Popocatépetl, and Ixtaccihuatl, far from being a menace and source of destruction, have been worth millions to the tourist trade of the country. Paracutín is, in fact, rather disreputable—something of a parvenu beside them. I decided that if the Professor insisted I'd let him and Silvanito go alone in the car.

It was long past midday, and the lake was far behind and below us. We were driving through empty arbutus-covered hills, broken here and there by the ubiquitous maize fields, now bare and dusty. In one of these we saw a vast number of black birds feeding. The passage of the car must have startled them, for suddenly they all rose together in a great whispering cloud and, as they wheeled away from the road, high over head, there were all at once displayed myriads of brilliant yellow breasts, transforming in a second an undulating black carpet into a vivid golden canopy.

"Species of oriole," said the Professor. "They make pocket-shaped nests out of bark. Isn't it time for lunch?"

Mrs. Fountanney unpacked bottles and glasses, and we stopped by the roadside, sitting on a rough stone wall while Silvanito got out the picnic. A thousand feet beneath us stretched a wide oval plain whose orchards and water meadows and little earthen lanes radiated from a chessboard village, dominated by the dome of a white church.

"They say," observed Silvanito, "that those of down there all own many cattle and are fat fat, and even a poor man eats fried udder for breakfast."

For Mexicans, Jiquilpan's one claim to fame is that it is the home town of General Lázaro Cárdenas, the reforming president of the Republic. Cárdenas nationalized the oil fields and the railroads; his wholesale expropriation of big landholdings created communal farms all over Mexico; to him was due the establishment of thousands of country schools; under him began the industrial drive which may yet restore to Mexico her position as leader of Spanish America. Today, he is the most criticized and, with the possible exception of Dolores del Rio, the most famous living Mexican. Jiquilpan has to thank him for many gifts and privileges, including the highway itself, and is naturally proud to be his birthplace and home. More important to me, however, was the fact that here too lived one Remedios Valdez and her daughter Candelaria.

"I know where they live," Silvanito had said. "In a very fine house that they rent from a man who sells wire of little barbs, and you can easily recognize it by the long stone bench outside and by the pepper tree; I know because Candelaria herself told me, and it is in the street of the Fifth of May and has a blue door."

We drove round the plaza a couple of times and after a few misdirections found the house. A woman with a skin the texture and color of potato peel appeared in the doorway wearing a freshly ironed dress of violet mirror satin.

"Could you tell me if Candelaria lives here?" I asked. "Candelaria and her mother, Remedios?"

"Oh, no, señor."

A gray turkey hen wandered out of the house onto the sidewalk, and the woman caught it by the long string that was tied to its leg.

"Could you tell me where they live?"

"That yes no, señor."

She was not in the least bit unfriendly. She picked up the turkey hen, tucked it under her arm, and stood smiling at me in silence.

"Well, I'm very sorry to have bothered you," I said. "My mozo told me they lived here—"

"Nothing of bother, señor." She paused to throw the turkey hen back into the house, and added, "You see, they do live here. That is to say, they did. But now they don't any more, pues."

"I particularly wanted to find Candelaria. She used to be my cook—"

"Oh yes, I know. And I'm her sister-cousin, but they've gone away and left me to guard the house."

She fingered the crimson zinnia stuck into one of the thick plaits of her blue-black hair and beamed at me.

"Could you tell me where they are?" I asked.

"Pos, yes. They're with my uncle's wife, that Agapita."

"And where does she live?"

The turkey hen walked out of the door again, and the woman put her foot on the string trailing behind it.

"In Tuxcala, puesen."

"And where is that?"

"Who knows," said the woman.

Out of the corner of my eye I could see the Professor getting more and more impatient in the back of the car, but I wasn't going to be stampeded.

"Is it far from here?"

The woman considered this for a moment, and then she said, "Oh yes."

"How far?"

"Much very far, señor. You go to Guadalajara, and you take a bus of the afternoon to San Isidro, and the journey lasts a whole day until nightfall, and a little moment after you leave San Isidro you come to a village where they make saddles of wood." She paused to draw breath and to push the turkey hen back into the house. "Then, when the bus stops, you ask if that's Tuxcala, and if they say yes, then that's where you get out."

She stood looking at me blankly while I was considering this, and then suddenly she brightened; her dark eyes glistened in her muddy brown face.

"I know," she said, with the air of one who has just successfully negotiated a complicated sum in her head. "Why don't you not go to Tuxcala at all? You can leave a message for them here with me. Already they sent to say that they were coming back, and they'll be here with all certainty by the end of the week—or by the day past tomorrow."

"And when did they send to say that?"

"Oh, soon after they went away. You see, they only went on a visit."

"And how long ago was that?"

The woman went into a short trance, staring at the ground. Then she looked up at me, and said, "Three months ago, señor, or two, or even very much more ago, pues."

I gave up and walked slowly back to the car. As we drove away, the woman stood waving to us from the doorway of the house; a grimy, mahogany-colored little boy was clinging to her spotless satin dress with one hand and picking his nose with the other. The gray turkey hen wandered past them out into the street and started to scrabble about in the gutter.

We turned off the main highway a little before sunset and entered on the last seventy kilometers of the steep and sinuous road to Uruapan. As we began to climb, the air freshened, and soon we were driving among pine forests beneath lofty crags. Here and there were meadows full of cattle, and once we passed a little sparkling stream. The villages too contributed to the Alpine atmosphere; their little houses were of adobe no longer but sturdily built of wood with widely overhanging eaves. By now the lamps were lit, and in their soft glow was a mellow feeling of comfort and cheerfulness. In the dusk you could imagine yourself back in the old Austria, scenting the sharp tang of resin and listening to the friendly buzz of talk by the Weinstube. Perhaps Maximilian too, when he paid his first state visit to Michoacán, which he described as the most troublesome province of his empire, took fresh heart in this mountain air and was carried back in memory to the great post highway from Vienna to Trieste.

The road wound in and out with unbelievable intricacy, past woods, over bridges, around a series of hills that all seemed, in the gathering gloom, to be of the same curiously familiar shape

—squat flattened cones, smooth and regular, their outlines blurred with a haze of pine trees. The sun had already set, but a faint glow remained ahead of us in the west.

"It looks as if we're catching up the sun, señor," said Silvanito, spitting tangerine seeds out of the car.

And indeed the light ahead was growing rosier, pulsating every quarter minute or so and giving the impression that behind the hills some titanic firework master was touching off, at fixed intervals, a chain of Bengal lights. Suddenly, however, one of them decided to act like a Roman candle. A burst of crimson light gushed over the summit of one of the flat-topped hills, setting on fire the clouds behind it.

It was our first view of the volcano, but the flames were still many miles away and only coincidence had placed the little peak directly between them and ourselves. One thing, however, was suddenly clear to me. Of course these hills were familiar. They were textbook volcanoes, familiar to every child who has had an illustrated geography primer. There they were, uniform in shape, diverse in size, hundreds upon hundreds of them swarming over the mountain country, an army of inverted cooking pans, cool now, but, no doubt, each in its day another Paricutín, carrying ruin and destruction over the whole state. For all Michoacán is of volcanic origin, and there is still a large waste area southeast of Uruapan, known as the Bad Lands, which, once a rich agricultural district, was turned into a desert by the sudden appearance two hundred years ago of the volcano Jorullo, in circumstances curiously similar to those attending the birth of Paricutín in 1943. Perhaps these violent and temporary volcanoes arise at fairly frequent intervals, safety valves for the whole region.

We left the red glare of the mountain behind us to the right, and as we ran downhill into Uruapan, twinkling lights began to appear through the pine trees below. The town lies in a fertile basin, famous for its flowers and orchards, but in the cold and feeble light of the street lamps its personality was austere, and the houses, whitewashed and tiled, seemed to crouch secret and watchful beneath their wide eaves. Although it was not late, there were few people about.

I had not stayed in Uruapan when I visited Paricutín some years before, but I knew of a hotel. Its appearance didn't promise anything luxurious, but we were all ready for bed and prepared to make the best of whatever accommodation it offered. I knocked on the modest wooden door, and then we waited. After about five minutes it was opened by a very small boy. He blinked at us for a moment, and then said solemnly and in English, "Tourist mansion! Come in! You will like to know it!"

The hotel had been in darkness when we went to bed and I hadn't noticed my surroundings. In the morning I opened my door onto a huge patio, a shining cloister filled with flowers—azaleas, begonias, geraniums, stars of Bethlehem, in row upon row of neat white classical vases, draped with foliage and crowned with color. Among the flowers were many bird cages filled with parrots, mocking birds, cockatoos, and budgereegahs. A flaming bougainvillea rioted along one wall, and among its crimson blossoms a family of white canaries sang and chattered—little white stars gleaming in the morning sun. After the severity of the hotel front this brilliance was startling enough, and the unexpected effect of space was heightened by the view through an archway of another patio overlooking a rose garden.

This element of surprise persists wherever the patio is the focal point of the house. Guadalajara has many mean-looking streets, but often enough the dingy, plastered façades and barred and shuttered windows conceal elegant and flowery courts. Where an American or North European house displays a bold front to the world, the charms of the Spanish home are turned inward as if jealous or scornful of the world's admiration. Withdrawn and reserved as the Spanish character itself, the patio has, all the same, older and more distant origins. Perhaps the courts of the Alhambra at Granada are the most renowned and elegant of Spanish patios, with their myrtles and fountains, their slender clustered colonnades and pavilions brilliant with mosaic and stalactite and multicolored stucco. But all these glories are concealed behind severe and frowning battlements, and all were the work of Islam. In the twisted lanes of Cairo or Damascus, or in any city of the Moslem world from Fez to the Indies, are innumerable homes, humbler Alhambras, reserved and exquisite, hiding from a world of violence and maintaining sacrosanct the privacy of the family. This was the way of life and the chosen type of abode that Spanish colonists took to their new lands, from Seville to Havana, from Havana to Mexico, from Acapulco to Manila, a way of life on which, long before the days of anthems and flags and all the other trappings of an imperialistic age, the sun never set.

The Fountanneys joined me for breakfast in the patio, among the flowers and the birds. The Professor had already been up and about for an hour. He was in great form and ordered three fried eggs with his ham.

The day was blue and brilliant. High above the rose garden Paricutín's white and lilac plume of smoke towered into the sky. After breakfast we explored the town. By day it was colorful and animated, displaying none of the mystery of the night before; hills rose on all sides and fir trees screened the view at the ends of all its cobbled lanes; everywhere there were flowers; down the main street one little plaza succeeded another, and in the gardens palms and pines, roses and plumbago and oranges and limes grew side by side; everywhere there were arcades, borne on slim pillars fashioned from pine trunks on square brick bases.

The market in Uruapan sprawls cheerfully through four or five steep and narrow streets, and so closely are the booths crowded together that they attain the effect of an oriental bazaar. The air is full of the scent of fruit, piled in mounds of every imaginable variety and color. There are nuts of all kinds arranged in neat little heaps, casseroles and cookpots of every size, laid out on rows and grouped in sets, little round white cheeses, and mats, fans and other types of plaited work. Where the last street merges into the plaza, we found the lacquer stores.

Lacquer is a specialty of Uruapan, which exports this ware

to every part of the republic and to the United States. A great variety of objects are made, from matchboxes to large trays, including many different patterns of gourd, bowl, and calabash, most of the forms being useful rather than purely ornamental. Lacquerware as made in China and Japan has many country cousins, from the delicate work on Srinagar papier-mâché to the gay, and sometimes crude, Pontypridd trays of early Victorian times. Uruapan ware is, in composition, more like the lac of Burma than true oriental lacquer, being made from the juices exuded by a plant bug related to the cochineal insect.

The best examples of lacquerware in Uruapan are treated with a kind of gesso or clay, and the designs are incised, picked out in colored pigment, lacquered, and polished by hand. The work is gay and brilliant and is characterized by a profusion of many-petaled surface flowers, but the designs, though often crude and barbaric, are robust and forceful, and occasional pieces are attractive.

Even before the days of the volcano, Uruapan had a tourist trade on account of its climate and its beautiful surroundings, including the famous waterfall of Tzaráracua, and the national park, which I particularly wanted to see. It is a large natural garden clinging to the sides of a gorge, through which, in foaming cataracts, rushes a clear, cold river. It lies a little way out of town, so we went there in the car, which we parked outside the gate, leaving Silvanito in charge of it, free to gossip with anybody who might pass.

The fact that there was no entrance fee may have had something to do with the air of neglect that hung over the garden, but perhaps this added to its charm. The paths were weed grown and heavily shaded by tall evergreen trees, and the undergrowth pressed thickly on either side. Save for the shafts of sunlight that thrust powerfully through the leaves every few feet, polka-dotting the path with slate and silver, the effect would have been most somber. However, in spite of the heavy scent of coffee blossom, the air was fresh, and there was none of the insect-peppered opacity that you find in tropical forests, where the sun's rays struggle with a haze of motes, like torchlight in a dark and dusty attic. The garden was wholesome and alive with the ripple of innumerable springs; its pellucid conduits, tinkling and artificial, ran merrily down the slopes of the gorge through a maze of fern-encrusted channels, their waters bubbling musically over pebble beds and swirling round mossy boulders. And above the myriad rustles and gurglings of the tiny streams, like the roll of drums behind an orchestra, the roar of the torrent was everywhere. Across the gorge was slung a sturdy wooden bridge, steeply roofed as if against Alpine rocks and snow, and here we sat down and looked about us. The setting was intimate, the details lavish. Beneath our feet the river churned and raced, massive boulders rumbling in its narrow bed. In and out, between the stony masses, darted a little flashing kingfisher, pursued, and evidently worried, by a pair of lilac-polled hummingbirds. All along the steeply sloping banks, in the shade of giant Indian laurels, were ranged huge banana plants, their tattered leaves anything up to a dozen feet in length, the largest I had ever seen.

And there was tropical color as well as tropical size. In the interstices of many trees there were orchids in bloom, clumps of delicate odontoglossum, and here and there a vivid queen cattleya. I like orchids and think myself fortunate in being able to see so many, for Mexico has a great variety and indeed is said to be the world's largest producer of the only species in general commerce—the vanilla. In some private gardens there are fabulous collections of orchids; here, in Uruapan, they were distinguished neither for their rarity nor their profusion, but the occasional exotic touches of color—rose pink, violet, cinnamon, and speckled chestnut—lent extra brilliance to the scene. Down below, zigzagging and hovering over the broken surface of the water, whirled dragonflies, blue and scarlet, green and puce, like vivid slivers of the lavish masses of bougainvillea and morning glory that festooned the treetops on either bank. High among the blossoms, their murmurs submerged in the thunder of the cataract, the bees moved drowsily.

Beside us on the bridge a student leaned against the coping, deeply absorbed in a mathematical textbook; a little way up the stream, in a natural rock basin, three naked Indio boys were frisking in the water, somersaulting and slapping each other with lily pads. Apart from these, there was no one in all Uruapan who cared to share this loveliness with us.

I had to give in about the volcano. The Professor was very keen to go, and since our way home went right past the dirt road leading to the mountain, it seemed rather mean not to start a few hours earlier and take him.

I had visited Paricutín in its younger days, and it had certainly been an alarming and brilliant spectacle. It had astonished the world by its sudden appearance, though, as is usual in such cases, there had been warning signs for some time before. There seems to be sympathy between volcanoes. The Neapolitans will tell you that when Vesuvius is quiet the mud volcano, the Solfatara, will be at its most active and that when the mud ceases to bubble they may expect the lava. Numerous portents heralded Paricutín's birth—earthquake shocks, subterranean rumblings, the sudden appearance and equally sudden disappearance of hot springs in the nearby mountains, and a minor eruption of the great peak of Colima. Then one day a Tarasco farmer, plowing his corn patch, was startled to see a jet of smoke gush up from a dip in the field a few yards away. The earth trembled, and as he watched, the cracks in the soil widened, the ground heaved up, and flames poured out with the smoke. A new volcano had been born. In a few weeks it had piled itself a cone hundreds of feet high, from which it spewed lava and hot boulders, and far away in Ajijic we could hear the dull rumble of the explosions. Soon after that I had gone there with Mexican friends. We reached the neighborhood late; darkness had fallen, and we should have missed the narrow track that led to the volcano but for the stream of cars creeping along it. The way was terrible, and with every bump we lurched from side to side, but, once started, it was impossible to turn back against the flow of cars. There seemed no reason why we should ever arrive anywhere. We could hear the explosions, but they sounded no nearer than they had done a couple of hours before. We could see a glow high in the sky, but round each corner we met only blackness again. For more than three hours we went on like this. Then, suddenly, we turned one more corner, the road opened out into a field, and there was the volcano, a dark regular cone with a firework show on top of it.

It was a fantastic sight. As though it were breathing, the volcano gave off deep resonant explosions, and with every breath there arose a shower of incandescent rocks. The larger ones were hurled out of the crater. The smaller, thrown straight up into the air, fell straight down again, but the volcano's agitated breath came so short that almost always, before they dropped again into those boiling depths, a new breath caught them, so that they bounced up and down like celluloid balls on a fountain in a shooting gallery. They were not all the same color, these flaming rocks and stones. Some were electric white, some were tinged with rose, and here and there one was red or sprouted fiery hair. The reverberations were continuous and the ground shook. From time to time there came a greater shock, and the larger boulders were hurled higher. Sometimes there came a little lull, and then the small bouncing stones, glowing duller and duller, would fall back into the crater. We stood directly beside a small lava stream, but it was still molten and had hardly formed a crust. The shaking body of the earth, the explosions coming like hurried breath, the tongue of lava, and the fiery spittings made it very easy to understand how man had invented his dragons. It was like being on the dragon's back, rather too near the head.

Later Paricutín changed character. First he poured out rivers of lava. Upon Parangaricutiro, the nearest large village, the lava advanced, and most of the inhabitants fled, taking with them the image from the church. The village was engulfed. Then he gave out dust, nothing but dust and more dust. More than a hundred miles away in Ajijic we were showered for several weeks with black grit, and all round the volcano there was desolation. In Uruapan, fields and orchards were blighted and the dust settled on the houses, on the roofs, on the sills, everywhere. It drifted through every crevice. It filled and fouled the ponds and pools, and the parched cattle died, choked to death. It killed the poultry. It even killed some children who had gone to glean in the stricken fields, a storming flurry of it catching and suffocating them. Then it rained, and a fine mud came through the air; then more dust, forming a treacherous cake over the mud. In the towns the roofs collapsed, and for days on end only a murky half light came from the hidden sun. Priests rode round the dark, choking streets in cars, standing on the running boards and calling the people to penance, to avert this retribution for their sins. From Uruapan, whither the first refugees had fled, people were now fleeing down the dim and muffled roads. This went on for weeks. High officials visited the region and relief was organized. Then the dust abated. No longer did it quench the sky. The lava still flowed but slowly. Experts prophesied that Paracutín would last only a few years, a nova among volcanoes. But all around it the country was a desert. This was what the Professor wanted to see.

Since my first visit the local authorities had done much to turn what was once the roughest of tracks into a practicable dirt road, and no doubt, if the tourist traffic had increased, further improvements would have been made. But what had been a torrent of cars had now, with the decreasing activity of the mountain, dwindled to a trickle. It only requires the appearance of a new volcano, an event reported mistakenly at least once a year, for Paricutín's tourist value to fall still further, and the road will crumble and eventually disappear back into the earth as adobes do. As it was, the going was rough. After a mile or more we came to an arroyo over which was a wooden bridge, some of whose planking for no apparent reason had been removed. Two small boys smirkingly directed us to a hamlet that lay off the road to our right, loudly demanding centavos and, to my surprise, matches. These small blackmailers were firmly repulsed by a flood of invective from Silvanito, and we lumbered down into the village, where I asked a man the way to the volcano.

"Who knows," he answered. No note of interrogation in his voice, no smile, nothing. A woman in a nearby doorway, ragged and emaciated, said coldly, "To the left." And suddenly, for the first time in Mexico, I was aware of what D. H. Lawrence called the "obsidian stare," impenetrable, defiant, and hostile. I am not in sympathy with Lawrence's attitude toward the Indios in their relations with the whites; I am more at home with earlier and less emphatic writers—with Mme. Calderón de la Barca, who notices everything and pontificates about nothing, or with Charles Macomb Flandreau, whose wit and penetration is always tempered with kindness and geniality. But here, in this remote Tarasco village, I could see eye to eye with Lawrence. There was hatred and mockery in the atmosphere. I suppose it was hardly surprising. To the Tarasco countryman the volcano has brought ruin, misery, and starvation. He has had no part in the profits of the hotelkeepers and taximen of the town, and it is only natural that he has little sympathy for the wealthy travelers who come in cars with lavish picnic baskets to chatter and gloat over the cause of all his troubles.

We were all glad to leave the village. At the corner the Professor asked an elderly man the distance to the mountain.

"I do not know the road to Paricutín," he said gravely, as though he were a stranger in a big city. "They say it is ten kilometers."

By the time we had gone nearly twice that distance, we had risen several hundred feet, crossed numerous rickety plank bridges, and changed a wheel. The sun had disappeared, and the sky wore an unearthly, sulphurous tint. Dust was in the air, in the car; dust grated between our teeth; the road, which had been steep and stony, was now muffled with gray volcanic dust, save where the deep ruts had a filling of red pumice. Through the ranks of sickly pines, tattered and moth eaten like half-fledged birds, wound sleek ribbons of gray silt brought down by the rains. It was some time since we had seen any animals, and the only sign of life was provided by a raven enjoying some nameless repast on a withered thorn tree. At our approach he heaved himself into the air and flapped clumsily ahead round a bend in the road, the scarlet flesh in his beak glowing against his plumage like the last live ember in a half-consumed coal fire. As we followed him round the curve, the landscape opened up into a slate-gray expanse fringed by ragged firs, and away beyond, squat and drab, crouched the volcano, a huge inverted flowerpot from which a mournful plume of gritty, dusty smoke poured into the still air.

The road ends a few kilometers short of the volcano, and if you want to get closer, you must go on foot or hire mules in the settlement of tumble-down shacks where those who have refused to leave the remnant of their fields now live. It was soon evident that Silvanito wanted nothing further to do with the mountain.

"The car will be quite safe, señor," he said in a tragic voice, "for I shall guard it."

"Don't you want to come with us?"

"Certainly that yes. But who knows if somebody might not put sugar in the gasoline, like that time in Guadalajara."

I looked around at the congeries of miserable huts with their two or three patches of gray and stunted corn. It was clear there was no sugar here to waste, but I made sure the gas tank was locked.

"But, señor," said Silvanito, rather pink, "it would be bad if we lost one of the little valves of the tires. For the doubts one must stay and watch the car."

Several small boys had appeared from nowhere to look at us, so I suggested giving one of them a few centavos to look after the car.

"I do not have confidence," said Silvanito, grandly, "in these of up here."

So we left him and started up the rough track, guided by a child who said he'd show us where to hire the mules. At a bend in the road I looked back; six small boys were clustered round the hood of the car gaping, while Silvanito expounded.

The mules were expensive, but our guide, a cheerful young native of the village of Paricutín, who introduced himself as Gerónimo López-to-serve-you, explained this by the fact that their food had come from many miles down the valley. As we rode along he talked.

"It came very slowly," he said, pointing to the tangled sea of gray-brown lava surrounding the half-submerged tower of Parangaricutiro's parish church. "Six months it took to flow, and now there are fifteen kilometers of it, or so they say."

In what is left of the village a few inhabitants still live. The Professor busied himself speculating about the effect of volcanic grit on the egg production of some scraggy hens we saw. I asked the guide if no one had been trapped in the village by the eruption.

"We all had good warning," he said, "though when that Dionisio, who first saw the smoke, came running to his neighbors, we didn't think much about it. You see, there was always a hole in that field from which the air blew very hot, and the boys would throw each others' sombreros into it so that they were cast back many meters into the air. It was a favorite game, so I for one didn't take Dionisio too seriously. But in the next hours there was much noise and smoke and fire, and the Señor Cura himself went up to look at it. When he came down the hill he called a meeting, and those of Paricutín came down to Parangaricutiro here, and we all put ourselves and our homes at the mercy of God. But later, when the dust and stones fell heavily and the ground shook, we were afraid to go into the church for Mass, for we thought it might fall down on us when we were inside. Of course, many people said it was a punishment for our sins, so naturally we were afraid, and we built a little chapel of wood outside. But now, as you may imagine, they say that if we had trusted in God more the lava would have stayed away from the village, but I do not think so."

He talked on, and the mules picked their way across the

jagged surface of the lava. Mrs. Fountanney rode easily, looking straight ahead, never speaking; every now and then she leaned forward and patted her mule's neck. The Professor sat rigidly on his mount, cross-questioning the guide and stopping every few yards to focus his binoculars.

From minute to minute the coughing of the volcano came louder, like the snarling of a lion, full of menace but without the terror of his full-blooded roar. Our guide said he thought it wiser not to go any closer, and at the summit of a little hillock we halted. The air was heavy and still, and across the valley the huge bulk of the volcano now appeared in its true impressive proportions. The Professor dismounted and set up the tripod of his camera. Thin white smoke, like incense before an altar, arose round the base of the mountain, from the narrow streams of hot lava that still crept from the fissures in its flanks. From the crater itself mushrooms of black smoke burst forth every few seconds, and, as they began to break up, the noise of the discharge reached us across the intervening space, like the muffled roar of cannon.

"We say in these parts," said Gerónimo, "that it's a poor fire that won't warm somebody's pot. But who knows."

Optimism is inherent in the Mexican character, and the Indio is the master of making the best of things. This had been rich land inhabited by a prosperous community. Now it was a lunar desolation. What the lava had spared was a desert of gray volcanic silt, flat and smooth as satin, save where the rain had worn small pinnacles beneath the pumice stones that speckled its surface, giving the appearance of a rash of tiny mushrooms. On all the hillsides around us the trees still stood in their serried thousands, but it was as if they had been blasted bare by many lightnings; stripped and sere, their stark trunks looked brittle as old bones, giving the hills the grizzled, spiny appearance of hedgehogs. This was not a mere pocking of destruction leaving untouched places; this was not a leveling of tree and building, leaving the old earth ready to receive seed and spore, and in a season to put forth new greens; here not a square inch was spared; this land was totally dead.

The Professor ran here and there, enjoying himself, sifting ash through his fingers, examining volcanic rock, poking at lava. Mrs. Fountanney and I stared in silence across the waste—grassless, birdless, insectless.

"Look at that low bough," she said, pointing to a ruined tree near the path. "You would have said, wouldn't you, that it was meant for children to swing on?"

And suddenly we both wanted to go home, back to the fertile Chapala lakeside. We called to the Professor, and, as we turned our mules to go, a little speck of white caught my eye—a poppy, barely rooted in the gray ash, was bravely struggling to put forth its one stunted flower. Perhaps Gerónimo's optimism was not so preposterous after all. Flowers don't give way to despair. Why should he?

On the way back to the highway in the car, we passed a tumble-down shack, ash colored amid the poisoned fields. A family was sitting beside it, a chocolate-dark Tarasco and his wife, a little girl, a boy of ten or so. They had a burro and some bundles, cookpots and two chickens crowded into a wicker cage. I stopped and greeted them. Only the man could speak Spanish, and the others muttered together in the harsh, guttural Tarasco tongue. I asked if any of them wanted a lift.

"Thank you, señor," replied the man, "but we have come home."

They would not change their minds. Hopeful and unreasoning as the little poppy itself, they were prepared for the struggle to strike new roots into their ruined homeland. We left them there, squatting amid the cinders, gray brown and desolate as the blasted earth, patient and dignified as the hills themselves, waiting for goodness knows what, goodness knows when.

Part IV: SPRING

40.

THE SUN had gone down, and the sky in the west turned to pink brass, and slowly to copper, to bronze, while overhead and to the north it was still plumbago blue, so vivid that you wanted to reach up and touch it. A man was fishing with his cast net on the shore, and I could see the charales splashing silver all round him as they jumped for flies in the mauve and orange water. Through the orange, black mud hens pulled rippling wakes of aquamarine behind them as they swam out to sleep in deep water, secure from marauding opossums and badgers and coyotes that hunt the lake edge at night. Slowly the lake changed to the sullen colors of gun metal, and the fisherman, throwing the catch from his last cast into his tall yellow basket, walked off up the village to sell the fish or eat them for his evening meal.

I had my own supper and went up onto the terrace to watch the night from there. I was smoking and had just flicked my cigarette butt at the clump of banana trees I always aim for when I was startled by a voice speaking at my side.

"May we come up?"

It was Guadalupe Paz and Doña Dimna.

"May we come up, señor?" chimed little Tiquico, capering along behind them carrying a basket.

"We come," said his father, "to repay you the loan of—ten

pesos was it, or only five?—and to ask you if you wouldn't like to buy these fish for fifty centavos."

Tiquico came forward and thrust the basket under my nose. It was so full of fish that I said I thought they were worth more than that.

"That yes, yes, señor," said Guadalupe Paz. "You see, it's like this; I was going to make you a present of them, but I had to go and fish before I could complete the ten pesos I owe you, and these are the fish I didn't sell, but with fifty centavos I can pay you all, and those that are over are a present, pues."

Suddenly all three of them sat down on the floor.

"We come, too, as we promised, to tell you what we plan to sow this summer—the months that enter would be the summer, wouldn't they?"

Many people will tell you that the Indios have no foresight and never plan things. It isn't true. They are often foresighted, and they make the most elaborate and optimistic plans. The trouble is, they don't carry them out. They get all set with a scheme to make their fortunes collecting bat manure at fifty centavos a liter from some new caves they've found, or for planting the surrounding hills with bamboo, and then someone comes along with an entrancing plan for sowing watermelons and sending them by truck to Aguascalientes (where they fetch a better price than in Guadalajara). So they start that, and then a brother suddenly falls ill, and they have to go and work his field for him across the lake in Tuxcueca. And when they come back the other schemes are dead, and one of them contracts to lay the foundations of a week-end house that a rich Mexican says he's going to build in Ajijic, and another, who doesn't fancy building work, becomes for a time a policeman in Chapala.

"Early in the summer," said Guadalupe Paz, "you take your weed hook and clean your corn patch once or twice or even three times—if God gives you license."

"Why must God give you license to do that?"

This was apparently a great joke, for they both roared with laughter, "Because, if he doesn't give it you, pues, your roof will leak with the first rains and you'll be too busy mending the tiles to do anything else. And then you sow a little chili."

Suddenly Tiquico gave a loud pipe of laughter and was silent.

"And some chick peas," added Doña Dimna. "That is, if God wills it and you have a mind to sow that year."

They prattled on. Their company was very restful after all the crowd I had met at Rendel's in Chapala that afternoon. I have noticed that God enters into the Indios' plans for summer sowing much more than at other seasons, and I have heard this attributed to the chastening effects of Holy Week and the fiestas of early May. It may be so. My visitors asked for another ten-peso loan, and then suddenly all three got up to take their leave.

"Pues, señor," said Guadalupe Paz, reaching in his shirt and pulling out some crumpled bills and some loose change. "Here is the money I owe you. But now, since you are kind enough to lend it me again, I do not give it you."

"Yes," said his wife. "Now that we have your ten pesos for the doubts, we shall start since at once watching the skies for three nights, and then if God allows it we sow our peanuts."

"What if he doesn't?" I asked.

"Then we give a little wait for the moon to change and watch the sky again."

"How d'you know what He says?"

"It is written in the clouds."

"And what if He says no again?"

"Then," said Guadalupe Paz, taking up the tale, "you'd better make a vow quickly—"

"Not a very strong vow," said Doña Dimna.

"You make a small vow, pues, and ask Him to forgive you for sowing your peanuts puesen."

41.

CAYETANO stopped beside me and gave his little cough.

"That Paz," he began, and stopped.

"How is she?" I asked. "I've been meaning to inquire about her. I suppose Primitivo's family is looking after her."

"That yes," said Cayetano. "But she is not happy."

"Why not?"

"Because Primitivo's mother, and his aunts too, are very strict and stiff, and they will not let Paz do this or that. They never let her go out alone, not a step, and they wish to do everything for the little Narcisito as they think it should be and not as Paz thinks."

"I see. Couldn't she go to her own people?" I asked, since the Indios change house and housemates frequently and easily.

"Yes," said Cayetano. "But then it would be hard for them, for they are not rich people, and they would have to feed Paz and the little one, and that is how I was asking myself whether Paz couldn't work here—instead of that Obdulia."

"But I can't fire Obdulia just to make a job for Paz."

"But Obdulia's leaving anyway."

In view of my suspicions about the fortune I was more relieved than not, and though Obdulia had said nothing to me about leaving it turned out that Cayetano was right.

"That's it," said Obdulia when I asked her. "It puts itself very sad here in the days of the week. I want to work in Guadalajara, where there are buses. I had meant to tell you, but somehow it didn't happen. I'm going on Friday, or one day with another in the week that enters."

Her pudding face became quite animated, no doubt thinking of the buses.

"And," said Cayetano, "the little Narcisito is only two, and if he played over by Candelaria's old house, he wouldn't give war."

So Paz came to work with us. She wasn't a very good maid, but she was a decoration about the house, and the Professor, who has an eye for womanhood, never complained of anything when she served at his table. She was as thin and quiet as a reed.

"Gracias," she said when I told her I hoped she'd be happy here.

"You're going to have that room in Candelaria's old house next to Lola, so you needn't feel frightened at night."

"Gracias," she said.

"Is there anything special the baby ought to have to eat?"

"Gracias," she said.

"Don't be afraid to ask. I'm sure you can say something other than gracias."

"Gracias," said Paz.

In the afternoons she would sit on the low step of her house playing with Narciso and singing him an interminable nursery song, whose words have no meaning:

> *Y aserrín*
> *Aserran!*
> *Los maderos de San Juan*
> *Piden queso*
> *Piden pan;*
> *Los de Roque*
> *Alfendoque;*
> *Los de Rique*
> *Alfeñique;*
> *Los de Trique*
> *Triquitrán—*
> *Triqui, triqui, triqui tran!*

I had various guests who stayed for short periods. Neill James, engaged on a new book, sent friends to me on more than one occasion when her little house of which she wrote so tenderly in *Dust on my Heart* was already full of visitors; then there was a very rich Arab who insisted on pitching a tent in the huerta to sleep in; a Greek widow who ran a dressmaking business in Torreón and sat all day long, like Lorelei, on a rock, combing her startling golden hair and humming to herself. And I had other guests who stayed for even shorter periods. There was a married couple who liked the place but couldn't be anywhere so isolated because they wished to revise their investments every morning; a French couple who were looking for "*une ambiance mexicaine,*" and, since they took no notice of the servants except to complain about them, never knew they had it; a teacher from Iowa, who left almost at once because we weren't gay enough and there was no dancing. There were people who wanted to get and pay more, people who wanted to get and pay less, and people who wanted to get more and pay less. There was a man who, seeing Lola ironing, took her sixteen pairs of trousers to press and made a loud scene when I charged him for this labor. But most of my guests were sensible, charming, and courteous, and their visits, like happy countries, had no history.

The Fountanneys came through it all swimmingly, the Professor accumulating masses of miscellaneous and quite useless information, and Mrs. Fountanney viewing everybody dispassionately under her arched brows and conversing in her cool, noncommittal voice. Fordyce snapped at everyone who addressed him so that his public appearances had the effect one might expect if a skeleton now and again emerged from its cupboard and stalked through the house.

This spate of guests meant that I was constantly having to go into town for small purchases of one thing or another and that I had less and less time for writing. I decided to try sending Silvanito.

Apart from the regular list of groceries, he was to bring a length of iron piping, some foie gras, a pair of scissors, Eno's fruit salts, a can of grease for the pump, six Waverley pen points, and a box of cough lozenges. He set off very early in the morning in Don César's bus, but before he left I gave him a short lecture on the temptations of the city, telling him to be sure and return by the same bus, which left Guadalajara shortly after midday.

At two thirty in the afternoon Don César's bus arrived back in Ajijic. Silvanito did not. Nor did he come by the four o'clock bus. Nor by the one after that. Nor on the last bus. He came at eight o'clock in a truck. I was sitting in my room with the door wide open and the light on when Silvanito came into the patio. He did not come to my room.

"Isn't the señor here?" he said brightly to Mrs. Fountanney, who was knitting quietly in an armchair. "I brought the medicines for the Señor Professor."

There was a short silence while, I supposed, he fumbled in his pockets and handed them to her.

"What would that be?" he asked.

"Fruit salts," said Mrs. Fountanney.

"Oh. And what would those other things be for?"

"They're also medicines."

"Ah," he said, and then added conversationally, "the Señor Professor knows to take many things, doesn't he?"

And since Mrs. Fountanney didn't answer, he started to play with the dogs. They made a great deal of noise, and Silvanito loudly called them by name several times to make quite sure I knew he was there.

"The señor is in his room," said Mrs. Fountanney.

"Oh."

There was a pause.

"Is he very busy?"

"I don't think so."

There was another pause. Then, "Would it be good to see him now?"

"You will know," said Mrs. Fountanney, who has learned to use the few Spanish phrases she knows like a native.

Silvanito slid across the patio to my room and knocked on the open door.

"Now I came, señor, pues," he said.

"So it appears," I answered bleakly. "Why are you so late?"

"The bus of Don César got away from me puesen."

"Then why didn't you come on the next one?"

"Pos, I missed that one also, puesen. But I brought the piping. It's up at Doña Arcelia's shop."

Silvanito was wriggling inside his clothes. His hands were clasped together on his chest under his miniature sarape, and he stood first on one foot and then on the other looking steadfastly at the tiled floor.

"And here is the little paste of liver, señor."

Indios will never carry anything if they can put it in a pocket, and they have an amazing number of pockets in the most extraordinary places, but still there never seem to be enough. Silvanito tugged so violently at the second can of foie gras, which was somewhere by his left hip, that his sombrero fell off.

"You shouldn't have had it on indoors in the first place," I said. "So now you can leave it there. Silvanito, I am very cross, you have behaved very badly indeed, and I shall not let you go to Guadalajara again."

"Yes, pues," said Silvanito.

He looked me straight in the face, blushed, and turned away to gaze at the window. There was a considerable pause.

"Did you bring the change?"

"Yes, pues. And the little pens."

He fumbled in his breast pocket and handed me the pen points. Several peso bills fell out onto the floor, and from half a dozen other places in his clothes he produced more bills, muttering from time to time, "Who knows," and "Pues," and "Pos," and "It is certain that I put it in there," and "Now where would it be puesen?" But when he had searched every conceivable hiding place a number of times—at one point he loosened his belt, peeked inside his trousers, and said, "No, pues," there were still ten pesos and thirty-odd centavos missing. And he hadn't brought the scissors.

"May I pick up my hat now?" asked Silvanito.

"Yes."

In the lining of the crown, Silvanito found another five-peso bill. He handed it to me with an air of triumph.

"There," he said, as if to indicate he had accounted for all the money.

"We'll forget the thirty centavos," I said. "So now you're only five pesos short. How much did you spend on yourself?"

"Pues," said Silvanito.

"Well?"

"Two pesos, or three."

"All right. I'll mark down three pesos to your account. Now you're only out two pesos, but we'll check the accounts again to make sure."

"Then I bought a shirt," said Silvanito.

"Ah. How much did that cost?"

"Four eighty," said Silvanito. "Or four thirty. It's very nice."

We agreed it would be fair if I charged him four fifty.

Then I asked why he hadn't bought the scissors.

"There weren't any," he said. "You see, I thought about them much when I was eating a taco of pork in the market for breakfast, and I thought that I would buy them in the afternoon, but when I got there they'd all been sold."

"Ah? So already at breakfast time you had decided that you wouldn't come back till the afternoon?"

This was too quick for Silvanito. He said, "No." And then added quickly, "But I bought the grease for the pump. Do I show it to you now?"

He went out into the patio and returned carrying something behind his back. He gave a little shy laugh.

"Look!" he said, blushing and holding out a vermilion shirt.

It was surprisingly well made, of thick fluffy cotton. On the chest was a large black S. The can of grease had been pushed into one of the sleeves, which had been knotted at the end, so that the can wouldn't slip out.

"It's a very pretty shirt," said Silvanito. "It's for football. And I'm going to keep it here and wear it after Mass on Sunday but in the afternoon."

42.

RENDEL decided to paint Mr. Humpel, and as Mr. Humpel would not leave his cooking or his baking or his parrots, Rendel sent round an enormous easel and worked on Mr. Humpel's veranda. He worked while Mr. Humpel went about his tasks. Rendel was fascinated by his turns of phrase and encouraged him to talk all the time. As I passed near the bungalow, I would hear the little groans dotting the sentences.

"For my breakfast I make eggs in fry form, boil form, or other form, and I read this report sent to me of a gold mine in Aguascalientes, and I take a piece of cake. Will you like a piece? It is the Streuselkuchen that Herr Chandos fonds. It is the philosophic life."

And another time he said to Rendel, "At the Chorros of Santa Ana there are thermal springs, where you will be much enjoyed."

Rendel commented later, "I went there—it's lovely, really lovely, you ought to go, Mrs. Fountanney, all hung with orchids—but nobody enjoyed me!" And his laugh split the air and echoed round the terrace.

He finished the picture, about half life-size, in a week, and there was Mr. Humpel, bending over his baker's oven, with the parrots making a diagonal flare of glittering green that caught a balance with the sitter's extended arm in its crumpled lilac shirt sleeve. It was exactly like him—but there was a twist to the gleam in the eye, a flick to the high light on the lip, and it was Mr. Humpel with sex appeal. To everyone's surprise, since he had been judged poor, Mr. Humpel at once bought the picture for five thousand pesos, paid in small notes out of a cornflake carton, and hung it in his bungalow, and every time he looked at it each little groan turned into a little chuckle.

"Na," he said, "it is well made. Once I was a fine boy."

More and more things at the inn seemed to need my personal attention. This time the ice hadn't come, and since I had ordered ice cream for supper, I went to Chapala to find out what had happened. When I arrived at the ice factory I found only an ancient, toothless hag in charge.

"The patron is out," she said.

"My ice wasn't delivered today. I want to buy some now. Have you some?"

"Yes, here it is."

She hobbled across the room and pointed to a large green door. I looked through the top shelf, which was screened, into a lead-lined cupboard. On the upper shelf were three blocks of ice.

"Is that big bit a whole bar?" I asked, "or only half a bar?"

"Who knows," said the hag.

"Or is it three quarters?"

"That's a quarter," she said, sucking her gums and pointing to the smallest piece of ice.

"But the big piece?"

She screwed up her eyes and poked her nose against the wire screening.

"I can't so-much it," she said. "What d'you think?"

"I think it's a whole bar. I want to take the whole bar and the quarter bar, the biggest piece and the smallest."

"That's the quarter bar, pues," she said, pleased with her own perspicacity and pointing once more to the smallest bit of ice.

"Yes, and can you sell it me?"

"Oh, yes."

"You know how much it costs?"

"Yes. Eighty centavos for a quarter bar. Most people buy quarter bars."

"And can I pay you? You're authorized to sell the ice?"

"How not? I'm in charge. The patron is out."

"Very well," I said. "Then I'll take the whole bar and the quarter bar. That'll be four pesos, won't it?"

"You will know, señor."

I paid her the money.

"Yes, that's right. My car's outside. I'll take it right away if you'll have it sent out."

"Ah!" she said, sucking her gums again and putting the money firmly in the till. "And how am I to do that? My patron is in Guadalajara, and he has the key of the cupboard, pues."

Eventually I succeeded in borrowing some ice from the Monte Carlo Hotel, which has never failed to help me in any difficulty of this sort, and as usual I remained for a drink on the terrace, looking out through the cool shades of its little park to the sunlit expanse of the lake and listening to conversation in four languages. It was after five o'clock when I got home.

The first thing I saw as I came into the patio was a pile of expensive luggage, topped by a lynx rug and a shining crocodile bag. Beyond it, in a rocker, sat a woman of about forty, very smartly dressed, her face darkly lit by huge tragic eyes. All the servants were standing round her, Apolonia grasping a glass of water, Cayetano gingerly holding a half-smoked cigarette, Nieves fingering the stopper of a small gold and crystal bottle, Aurora with a mink coat draped over her arms, Paz bearing in both hands, as if it were a holy image, a leopard-skin purse.

"Here, here comes the señor!" they all cried.

The woman turned her somber searchlights on me and broke into French.

"*Monsieur, je suis épuisée, éreintée, rendue*—I am exhausted, worn out, dead. I am Varia Palavandova. Monsieur, you who understand the heart of a Russian, lead me, I beg you, to where I may repose myself."

With a brilliant circular smile for us all, she stood up and waited to be led. She had very beautiful teeth, small and shapely. I had done my best to make the house comfortable, and, for Ajijic, I thought I had done pretty well. But I doubted whether it would be up to Mme. Palavandova's standards. I led her to the best, the largest room. I had been pleased with its lettuce-green tiles and oyster walls, but when she came into it, it looked very rustic. We were followed by Cayetano, still carrying the cigarette, and by Apolonia with the glass of water. Behind them Nieves opened the little bottle. She sniffed quietly and choked loudly over the smelling salts. Mme. Palavandova laughed. She expressed herself delighted with everything, asked the price of nothing, said how chic the sacking curtains were, requested that a maid be allotted entirely to her service, and accepted my invitation to cocktails later on.

The servants were impressed. With tense, whisperful bustle all the new guest's things were taken to her room in record time.

"And a coat like this," said Aurora, stroking the mink. "It must need the skins of many little rats to make it. Or would they not be rats?"

"Perhaps they're tlacuaches of the North," said Nieves.

I detailed Paz to the duties of lady's maid, and for the next hour the house was on its toes. Mme. Palavandova asked for mineral water, a hot bath, China tea, and aspirin, six extra towels, a footstool, a note of the latest news on the radio, a bowl of ice cubes, three more pillows, a copy of *Vogue*, and a wire brush for suede shoes, almost all of which we were able to supply. By chance Mrs. Fountanney had a three-year-old *Vogue*, and we sent that. There had once been a wire brush, but investigation revealed that Apolonia had used it as a saucepan scourer. I sent a big vase of wild flowers instead.

No further messages arrived for another hour, and then, just as the sinking sun's rays, which flood the veranda, changed from yellow to rose, Mme. Palavandova appeared, trailing clouds of chartreuse chiffon, smiling brilliantly and relentlessly speaking French. She acknowledged introductions to the Fountanneys, draped herself into a chair, adjusted a clang of bracelets, accepted a cocktail, and lit up her great murky eyes.

Professor Fountanney, with little red spots on his stretched cheekbones, spoke, slowly and faultlessly, the French of Racine and did his best to make himself agreeable.

"You, monsieur," said Mme. Palavandova to the Professor, "you who understand the heart of an artist, imagine to yourself how exquisite it is, after a tour such as I have completed, to find at once tranquility, beauty, and comfort."

Her smile indicated that the Professor and I were joint authors of the view, the quiet and the plumbing. She threw away her half-smoked cigarette, which lodged against Mrs. Fountanney's shoe.

"*C'est formidable,*" said Mme. Palavandova.

Professor Fountanney cleared his throat to speak, but just then Aurora shuffled hurriedly onto the terrace, crying, "Señor, señor! There is a bat in the room of the new señorita, and Cayetano can do nothing, nor can that Paz, and Nieves has hidden her head in the pink bag of the señorita, and the bat does not want to come out of the room, not for anything, so what shall we do?"

"Dear, dear," said the Professor.

Mme. Palavandova's eyes shone with dark fire.

"*Une chauve-souris? Mais je les adore!* Their dear little hands!"

In a swirl of chiffon she was gone, and when I reached her room, she had the bat clasped between her palms and was murmuring endearments to it in Russian. In one corner stood Cayetano, hat in hand and looking shamefaced, and in another

Nieves was slowly emerging from a ruffled satin pillow cover.

"It doesn't matter, not at all," said Mme. Palavandova, as Nieves stared ruefully at the crumpled satin. "Imagine, the boy was throwing his hat at the poor little beast. *Mais, ma pauvre chère petite chauve-souris,* you must go out into the beautiful big night which is yours."

And, flying to the door, she flung her chiffon-streaming arms wide, and with a high cheep the bat swooped off into the darkness.

"It doesn't understand itself how she caught it so easily," said Cayetano when Mme. Palavandova had returned to the terrace. "Those animals don't lend themselves to being caught."

"The señorita is much very valiant," said Aurora, "for bats are dangerous, but more so if one is asleep and dreaming."

And as I returned to the veranda, I heard Mme. Palavandova saying, "But, monsieur, you who understand the heart of a friend of nature—"

During the evening the entire household had been involved in attending to the needs of our new guest—all save one. At midday the following day, I saw her too, leaning on her broom in the passage outside the best bedroom and contemplating with some curiosity the chief trophy of her morning's cleaning, a shell-pink hairnet.

"It sees itself that the señorita's hair is of the most rare color underneath," said Lola, looking up. "Won't you lend me a hundred pesos?" she added inconsequently.

"No."

She carefully stowed the hairnet in a small pocket of her apron and grasped her broomstick firmly with both hands.

"They make me much lack, pues," she said.

I said a hundred pesos was a lot of money to lend to anyone. I said it was far too much.

Lola waddled a few steps along the passage and swept away a cobweb with her broom. Then she came back and stood in front of me, looking at the floor. She sighed.

"You see, señor, it's like this. The money's not for me. It's for my brother-in-law; that's to say it's for my sister so that she can give it to him so that he won't sell her little pigs. She loves her little pigs." Lola paused and sighed again. "You see, my brother-in-law owes some money to a señor who makes candles and isn't very nice, and the money's for that señor, and if he isn't paid he'll make my brother-in-law sell his mound of maize on which my sister feeds her pigs, but now he won't let her have any more of it and he wants her to sell her pigs instead."

Lola gave a tremendous belch.

"I'll lend you ten pesos," I said.

"Thank you, señor," she replied. "You are generous and noble. And, d'you know, I've just been thinking, and I don't think I'll lend them any money after all. My brother-in-law is very rare. He prefers his maize to his señora's little pigs."

Out on the terrace they were drinking sherry.

"It's a very curious thing," Professor Fountanney was saying. "The Romans of the expansion of the Empire, who were, I think nobody will deny, virile, were anxious that every hair should be plucked from their bodies. Nowadays, however, they tell me there are charlatans who extort money from my male compatriots on vain pretexts of promising them a growth of hair on the chest. Indeed, hair on the chest is perpetually referred to in advertisements, fiction and illustrations—a sort of symbol of sexual potency, which it by no means necessarily indicates—and I have heard that a modern writer, whose name is of no great consequence, made a disagreeable scene in a publisher's office when a critic had accused him—only, indeed, in a purely literary sense—of wearing what I may call a chest-wig. What am I to conclude from all this?"

"My dear Professor," said Mme. Palavandova, "I have been married six times, three times to Americans. And I could tell you."

"What?" asked the Professor.

"Your wife . . ."

"Go right ahead," said Mrs. Fountanney. "American over-compensation, Logan. I am always telling you."

"My wife has become imbued with— But never mind, go on, madame," said her husband.

"I divorced the Frenchman for infidelity, the Italian because he wanted me to bring up his illegitimate children, the Spaniard because he was always catching chills—"

"Chills?" questioned the Professor.

"Yes. Returning across the patio from the maids' bedrooms."

Mrs. Fountanney chuckled.

"And what did you divorce the Americans for?" she asked.

"The alimony, of course," said Mme. Palavandova.

"There, Logan, take care," said Mrs. Fountanney.

Palavandova's visit, more than anything else, served to draw attention to our poor communications. Every day she wanted to send a cable, or had a registered package to collect, or required some object unobtainable anywhere nearer than Chapala, thus necessitating repeated short trips by car or involved negotiations, generally unfruitful, with the friendly but unreliable driver of Don César's bus.

Then, the day before she left, a dreary-looking telephone box appeared in the post office. It was made of mustard-colored wood and was chipped and stained. It remained there for some days.

"They sent it from Guadalajara, señor," said Joaquín, the postmaster, "from one of the post offices there."

Sometime later a modern French telephone was installed in the box. At first it wasn't quite certain through which end you spoke and through which you listened, but the comisario knew, and he spent several hours every day speaking to Chapala on important business. On Saturdays, furthermore, the instrument was reserved exclusively for him. Then for two weeks no one could telephone because the line was down somewhere near San Antonio, and the head office in Guadalajara was too busy to send and mend it.

When it had been repaired, I went up to the plaza one day to telephone the drugstore in Chapala. Three times I asked for Chapala, and three times they connected me with Jocotepec, at the other end of the lake.

"It appears it wants to go the other way," said Joaquín. "All the calls are going in that direction today. The little bell sings high high each time, and that means it's from Chapala toward Jocotepec. Yesterday it went the other way—all day long the same way, like the buses on a saint's day. It's a pity, pues, it wants to go to Jocotepec today. I suppose the drugstore there wouldn't do?"

I said it wouldn't.

In the afternoon I tried again, this time with success. When I had finished speaking, Joaquín said, "And one day of these, señor, they're going to connect us with the main line, and you will be able to speak to anywhere in the republic. That is, anywhere that has a telephone like this. And then you won't have to telephone to Chapala any more."

"Why not?"

Joaquín looked at me amazed.

"Because then, pues, you'll be able to speak to Guadalajara, or even as far as the capital."

Palavandova stayed one hectic week, and for the next fortnight everything ran smoothly. The Professor's stomach remained in order; the servants didn't quarrel; nothing of much value was broken or lost. I had been working very contentedly on a story. It is very agreeable to live thus for a time with people one has invented, manipulating them, or trying to prevent them manipulating themselves in ways one doesn't wish. The story was going very well and was about two thirds done. Then four guests arrived.

They were an American couple and an American of German origin with a Mexican wife. They were extremely nice. They had come for a holiday, and they seemed thoroughly to enjoy themselves. They entertained constantly. They bathed and chattered and played cards, and the whole house was full of a good-natured jolliness. They didn't seem to care what they paid, and they liked everything. They were as pleasant and easy guests as one could wish. But that was the end of my work. They stayed three weeks, and when I got back to my story, it was a poor and lifeless thing. I had lost the thread. The characters were flat-faced puppets, and nothing I could do would tempt them back to life.

I ought to have been delighted with the way things were going. With the Fountanneys, Fordyce, and Mr. Humpel, the place ran, making a little money and justifying the setup. Extra guests brought good profits, especially short-term guests for a month or less, who paid full prices. That had been a very good three weeks for me. But I wasn't in the least pleased with it. I was lamenting my story.

43.

I WENT out in the late afternoon and strolled along the beach. It was a day of white, dry sunlight, and the loop of an incoming seine net had caught some water hyacinths in a sharply outlined arabesque, lettuce green against the whitish mirror of the lake. The bodies of the Indio fishermen glowed—hot copper with fire reflected in it—against the green. One of them plunged his arms into the hyacinths and threw great armfuls out over the net, over the bobbing twinkling floats, armfuls of green into the glassy air. Venustiano, completely recovered now, was sitting in the dappled shade of a willow tree watching his two cows, his horse, and the big black ram drinking together at the water's edge.

"My ram's been sick, too," he said, "but he got well in four days, without making a vow."

A little way off, Venustiano's nephew Chui and the sharecropper, the man who worked for half the produce of the land he helped to cultivate, were winnowing corn in the soft evening breeze. They had spread out a big petate, and they had a tall basket beside it full of the corn to be winnowed. From the big basket, Chui filled two smaller flat ones, exchanging the full for the empty with the sharecropper with the precision of a man tossing bricks. The sharecropper heaved the full basket high above his head and tilted it, pouring out the corn. Hoisting the full basket was not at all a light job. As it tilted, the grain fell heavily onto the mat and the evening wind obligingly blew away the light chaff. The two young men worked on a steady swinging rhythm that lent their work the quality of a dance. The whole scene was charmingly colored: their wide yellowish hats, floppy white pajamas; the coppery skins and the chaff's light brown, the grain's honey yellow and the rush mat's silvery green standing clear against the pale blue and white of the lake. Like most Indios at work, they were graceful. Nothing was done for the look of the thing; everything was strictly functional, even to the flick of scarlet given to the scene by the handkerchief Chui had tied over his mouth to keep out the flying chaff. Nobody thought of the winnowing as beautiful, and nobody on the shore looked at the two men at work, except the pretty daughter of Don Fidencio, and she was looking at Chui. She had lingered behind her father, who was taking his evening stroll to the end of the jetty.

Venustiano looked reflectively at the short stumpy figure of Don Fidencio.

"He has often borrowed money from me," said Venustiano. "In fact, he still borrows money from me. Yet he is by much the richest man in the village. Richer than that César, oh, yes."

"Then why does he want to borrow money?"

"Pues, he is afraid of the bandits."

Venustiano brushed a small scrap of blown chaff off the black, broken nails that stuck out of his toeless huaraches, and went on:

"Many years ago, pues, his aunt's husband, old Don Agripín, who lived over in Ixtlahuacán, was taken one night with his son Emigdio by the bandits. They took him to the mountains and sent a message to Doña Cruz, Don Agripín's wife and Don Fidencio's aunt, asking for five thousand pesos ransom. Now old Don Agripín had money, but he didn't want to part with it. He had foreseen that one day he might be taken by the bandits, and he had told his wife that if that happened she was to give half the ransom asked. He was a great bargainer. So Doña Cruz paid two thousand five hundred pesos to the man sent by the bandits and waited. The man came back the next day and demanded another two thousand five hundred. Doña Cruz was a dutiful woman, and, after thinking it over, she gave the man another one thousand two hundred and fifty pesos. That seemed to be obeying her husband's instructions. She said that was quite enough and she wouldn't give any more, and the man, after some argument, went away and Doña Cruz waited. She waited for nearly a year, pues, and then they found Don Agripín and young Emigdio up in the mountains. They had been tied to trees with wire and left there, and when they were found, their bones were as bare as a peeled branch."

Venustiano paused to light a cigarette while two women in profound, black-stockinged mourning walked by with wash baskets on their heads. One basketful was wrapped in brooding blue, the other in burning lilac.

"So of course Don Fidencio is nervous. He was his Uncle Agripín's heir, and he still owns the property out at Ixtlahuacán as well as his land here. But I think he pays money to the government not to have his taxes raised. He must have quite eighty thousand pesos in silver as well as his property, but I don't know where he keeps it. He does not like to be thought rich. Even when his elder daughter married, he did not have much of a feast, so I don't know what good his money does him. Of course bandits aren't what they used to be. But still, some bandits did once come and take Don Fidencio to the mountains. They came about seven, just when the light was going—you know, they always come then, so as not to be recognized—and they came galloping into the village firing their guns. But that was many years ago, pues, and by nine o'clock he was back at his house with two of the bandits to whom he paid four thousand pesos in silver then and there. That was not very much for him. They might have asked much more."

Venustiano blew some more chaff off his hand onto his white pajamas and clucked to one of his cows who had strayed down the shore.

"It was soon after that that he came to borrow off me for the first time. And ever since, two or three times a year, he comes along to my house, bringing a few peons with him. He falls on his knees, and sometimes he weeps, and he cries, 'Don Venustiano, for the love of God, lend me fifty pesos!' or it may be seventy or even a hundred. He does it usually when his taxes are due. Yes, he, a rich and educated man, grovels on the floor and weeps in front of his peons. And then, you see, they speak about it, and the word goes round that Don Fidencio is not really rich at all, but quite poor, a man who must come to me, poor as I am, and borrow fifty pesos for his taxes. And the bandits have never been near him again."

The light was fading and the lake had turned silver with big smudges of smoke gray. Chui and the sharecropper had finished winnowing that lot of corn. They had put it into the big basket, and they had folded up the straw mat. Old Encarnación, Nieves' grandmother, who is very poor and a persistent beggar, was beginning to pick over the chaff in search of a few grains of corn. Don Fidencio and his daughter walked slowly back from the jetty. The daughter went very slowly. She would reach the narrow street to the village just as Chui, carrying the two small baskets and the mat, reached it too. The sharecropper staggered under the big basket full of grain. In a garden up the street two guitars began to thrum below two high, strained voices.

"Of course," said Venustiano, "if that Chui marries his daughter, Don Fidencio and I will be relations."

"And do you always lend him money?" I asked.

"Oh, yes."

"But then don't the bandits get the idea that you are the rich man? Don't they ever trouble you?"

"Me?" said Venustiano, his whole face wrinkled with surprise. He got up and flung his nut-brown sarape over his shoulder. "No, they don't bother me. You see, the chief of the bandits and I are compadres. We are very closely related. No, they don't trouble me, pues."

44.

I SUPPOSE Rendel's interpretation of Mr. Humpel, and, more especially, the latter's evident satisfaction with the portrait, should have done something to prepare me for the bombshell that arrived one morning with my breakfast. There was some whispering outside my door, and I could just hear the voices of Apolonia and Cayetano in the kitchen, raised in fierce discussion. Nieves brought in my coffee, saying good morning as usual but carefully avoiding my eye and fixing her own gaze on the note beside my plate as if she were trying by sheer concentration to divine its contents.

Sir! I write to advise, since the little Paz is too modest to say it herself, that she may not work more as service-maiden, for she is my Bride. Before many days, I bid you as honored guest to the wedding which will be in Guadalajara. To many it can appear the old man's folly, yet my heart is in the Maytime. Will you be so kind to tend my papagays while the wedding journey, which we think to make with bus to the Capital? I thank you.

I went straight to Mr. Humpel's bungalow to congratulate him. Paz was there, sitting on the edge of a chair and blushing under the pale rosewood of her skin. There, too, were her parents and a number of other relatives.

"Now that we are promised, the old ones will not leave us," said Mr. Humpel cheerfully. "It is their custom."

For days Ajijic buzzed with the news. I had grown fond of Mr. Humpel, and there was no one in the village but had a soft spot in his heart for Paz; yet the news gave me considerable misgiving, shared, I thought, by Cayetano.

"Her life will now be most secure—" he paused. "You forgive me, señor, I do not mean disrespect, but in the place of Primitivo the Señor of the Oven, though a most kind gentleman, will be like an ancient mule in the harness of a fine young horse."

The other servants and, indeed, most of the women of Ajijic looked at Paz as if she were transfigured.

"It is very good for her," said Aurora, "very good. And think how nice is the life of a young widow—rich."

The foreigners prophesied disaster, and one woman went so far as to call on Mr. Humpel and tell him exactly what would happen.

"She asks how I will see many brown babies, perhaps not by me fathered," he told me later. "But I answered I will no babies for I wish not to plant my issue forth so mixed, and I shooed her. Na, na, I am old and the little Narciso is for me family enough."

I did not know Mr. Humpel's eventual plans, but I thought it likely that, in view of the old man's evident intention to accommodate the bulk of Paz's family, he would be planning to leave me. To make matters worse, a few days later Nieves announced that she would be leaving for good within a month. She had insensibly become head housemaid, instructing all new maids in their duties, and saving me much trouble. But for many years she had been contributing from her wages toward the education of her brother as a priest, and now at last, in June, he was to be ordained. It is a social step up to have a brother in the priesthood, and it had always been her dream to keep house for him. In fact, she was going to be a lady, the sister of the padre, a person of importance in any village. And even though she had heard that he was to be sent to Campeche, which, so they told her, was full of dangerous serpents, she was already making eager preparations.

Suddenly it seemed as it sometimes does in Mexico that everything was conspiring to make life disagreeable. Day by day the weather grew hotter, the air dustier, and tempers more uneven. My next problem was Apolonia. She had never been really satisfactory, spending far too little time in the kitchen and trying to do everybody's job but her own. Furthermore, of all the things she could do, she excelled least in cooking. She smashed something every day, she had a heavy hand with seasoning, and I could never make her see the advantage of keeping a separate frying pan for omelets.

"I washed the pan with ashes, señor," she would say brightly, "and they were hot, hot and red from the fire. But it still smells of fish, doesn't it? And don't I throw a little coriander into the wet soup of liver?"

I said I thought liver had enough flavor of its own.

"I have always done it that way," she said, chewing her bubble gum. "No coriander?"

"I don't like coriander."

"You will know, pues. It won't have any flavor without coriander."

She made herself agreeable to the other servants, but they all disliked her and never missed an opportunity to bitch her.

"She comes from over the hill," said Cayetano. "They're bad people over there. That's the village where the bandits come from."

"That Apolonia," said Lola, "says she knows to do many things, but she washes the plates with soap, and the flavor falls bad to me. I am ill; I cannot eat here any more."

"And she has broken many of those little cups of two sides we use for eggs," said Nieves. "I saw her. She is great finisher off of dishes."

"She likes men," hissed Aurora. "Don't say I said so, señor, but that's why Obdulia left."

I didn't take much notice of what they said, but a day or two later, passing the rubbish pit, I noticed all the bits of broken ollas and casuelas, and thought it was time to speak to Apolonia about it again.

"You really ought to take more care, you know," I said. "This earthenware is very fragile, and everything is much more expensive now."

"Pues," said Apolonia with a sigh, "it gives me much pain to tell you, señor, but on Sunday I leave for my village. My village is ugly, very ugly, but I say it's pretty because it's my home, and there I have a field of tomatoes. And everyone there is healthy, they stay well—that is, if God wills it. And everywhere there is much water, a river that hardly ever dries up and many little eyes of sweet water so fresh and so blue that you might think it was—I don't know how to say it—so blue you might think it was full of white soap. And at the entrance of the barranca there is a rock, and all day long it is weeping water. Oh, yes, you can get there by bus and it is called Saint John of the Little Straw Mats. Sometimes people even go there on purpose."

I said I was sorry she wanted to leave.

"I am sorry, too, señor, about the dishes. But what would

the poor dish makers do, puesen, if we didn't break a dish from time in when? I know about dish making, pues."

45.

OBDULIA suddenly arrived back from Guadalajara, and I told her she could work for me again, starting the following week when the Humpels were due to return from the capital. But Obdulia was no cook, so I went to Chapala to find someone to replace Apolonia.

"A cook?" they said. "Yes, there are several good cooks here. But Enedina and Jacinta are not here, they are working in Guadalajara, and Luisa doesn't work any more, and Pabla is with the American señorita over there, and Consorcia is working at the Hotel Niza. Consorcia is a very good cook. She knows how to make pie. Why don't you go to the Niza and just walk through to the kitchen and ask her if she doesn't want to leave the hotel and work for you?"

Servant stealing is not viewed here with disapproval but rather as an indoor sport. Nevertheless, I did not feel equal to invading the hotel and shanghaiing their cook.

"Then why not send little Chepe here?"

All this happened when I was sitting at the Widow's cantina, which is a good central position in which to establish oneself while sending boys on errands. After a little while Chepe came back and said Consorcia wasn't working at the Hotel Niza any more after all.

"Ah. Then who knows where she'd be."

"She went to Guadalajara, to work there."

"No, she didn't. Or better, she did, but only for the day."

"There's old Dionisia. She has cooked for foreigners."

"And where does she live?" I asked.

"Up there."

I sent Chepe to look for old Dionisia and meanwhile went to do a little shopping myself. In every shop I asked if they knew Consorcia and where she was. Everyone knew her, and all agreed that she was a good cook. But nobody knew where she was to be found. The women in the cooperative store didn't know either. But suddenly a man at the far end of the counter beckoned to one of them and whispered to her. She came back to me.

"This one knows where she is."

"You know?" I asked, turning to him. "Can you find her for me this morning?"

"How not."

He beckoned and whispered again to the woman behind the counter. She nodded brightly to me.

"How not," she said. "He's her son-in-law."

I asked him to bring her to the Widow's and, when I had finished my jobs, went back there myself. Chepe was waiting. Old Dionisia was sorry, but she couldn't come to work for me because she couldn't leave her own house, where she had charge of three infant grandchildren, and because she was lame and because she was working in the fields.

I waited. The sunshine glittered on the sandy beach and the little white boats and the gay awnings with steamer chairs under them. A neighbor came by and dumped a load of the latest gossip. Some boys tried to sell me some hideous picture post cards. I bought a few avocados from an old woman who also tried to sell me yesterday's newspaper and a broken toy violin. Time went by.

Then I heard a brisk step, and a tall woman marched up to my table and said, "I am Consorcia García, at your orders."

I liked her at once; she had a humorous aquiline face and

she talked to the point without all the usual circumlocutions and conditional clauses of the Indio. She was perfectly decided about what she could do and what she expected to be paid. We agreed quickly. I arranged for her to come the day of Apolonia's departure.

"It is very good," she said and marched off with long steps, her aquiline profile high.

I was to go to Chapala to fetch Consorcia on Sunday, but at seven in the morning she arrived in Ajijic.

There drew up before the door a rubber-tired cart, drawn by one horse and one mule. In the cart were a dozen sacks of charcoal for Venustiano, a few hundred bricks for Don Bernabé and some sacks of cement for me, a pile of planks for Doña Arcelia and two cane armchairs, one of which had been broken on the way, while in the other Consorcia was sitting under a stout black umbrella, with bags, baskets, and bundles arranged around her. There at once began a tussle about her fare. She was perfectly good-humored and jollied the owner of the cart along, treating him, though he was an elderly sourpuss, as if he had been a comely youth.

"What, lad? One peso fifty for that little ride? And I perched up like a bird and thrown from side to side at every rut? And didn't I make you laugh? And my chair leg broken? Ah, good morning, señor, here I am, with all and junk. Come now, lad, take the peso I promised you."

But, cajole as she would, it cost her one peso twenty-five.

"What a man, what a hard elbow he has," she said. "I hope your wife sleeps along the wall and kicks you out of bed, lad!" she called to him. Then she turned to me. "Now I'm quite ready to start making breakfast."

Consorcia fitted into the household at once. There was no doubt that she was a very good cook indeed. And she was enormously active. In the afternoon, when the toils of lunch were over, she would sit on the steps of the kitchen, but that would soon pall, and she would sweep the paths or help Silvanito water the vegetables. The Professor's diet sheet did not faze her at all.

"It understands itself at once," she said. "Paps and gruels and all things soft. Like a child's, the señor's stomach has no cooking."

For a fortnight everything ran like clockwork. Then Consorcia asked if she might spend Saturday night in Chapala to see her family. It happened that on the Sunday the Fountanneys were going out, and I arranged with Consorcia to leave everything ready for Sunday lunch, some things cold and some things that Nieves and Obdulia could easily finish between them, so that Consorcia need not return until Sunday afternoon. I thought she well deserved a day off. She left everything in perfect order. But she did not return until ten o'clock on Sunday evening, and then she was very tight. She came with several friends escorting her and was persuaded to go to bed in her room. Until very late long monologues and snatches of song echoed out over the night air, and in the morning Consorcia looked terrible, her face fallen as if it had been boned and her big eyes shadowed in black circles. But she did her work as usual, and I said nothing.

The week went by smoothly and on Saturday Consorcia said, "Today I do not ask permission to go. Thus I punish myself."

Then she cleaned out the tool shed.

Supper was late that night, and for some reason Consorcia brought it in herself. The dishes were well cooked, but Consorcia was walking with a very lightsome tread. I remembered that she had been out for an hour and a half buying salt, and that the cantina is not far off. I hoped for the best. If she had gotten a little tight, the effects would be diminishing by now. But drink didn't take Consorcia that way. Its effects were cumulative. She brought in the coffee, looking gayer than ever. And suddenly she waved her arms in the air, and broke into a gay little dance round the dining room, chanting blithely, "It's Saturday night! It's Saturday night! I always like Saturday night, don't you, lad?"

She was talking to the Professor, and for an awful moment I thought she was going to chuck him under the chin. But she merely continued her fandango, knocking over a chair and coming into collision with a table, chanting "It's Saturday night!" until a tile more polished than the rest betrayed her and she fell flat on her face. She seemed quite unhurt and Cayetano managed to haul her to her feet and steer her out of the room.

The Professor had viewed all this with a surprised smile.

"Oh, dear, oh, dear," he said. "I think that was very funny."

"I should think that on Saturday nights you'd better give us boiled eggs and her a mug of tequila," said Mrs. Fountanney.

"She's well worth putting up with," said the Professor.

Another week passed by and Consorcia excelled herself. She made cakes and pies, and she produced a most elaborate wreath of aspic with buried treasure of chicken, eggs, and vegetables gleaming in its depths. On Saturday I suggested she should have the evening off.

"Then I would like to go to Chapala," she said.

Once again she left Sunday's lunch nearly ready, and we got through the day without mishap. This time she did not return late. She did not return at all.

I woke to see Nieves standing uncertainly at the foot of my bed. It was a white, sultry morning, an unfriendly morning. Nieves' face wore a look of disaster.

"What shall we do, señor?"

I blinked at her sleepily.

"Consorcia hasn't come, pues," she said, "and although it is still early, the Señor Professor has already asked for his hot water, and what shall we do?"

I told her to get the fire lighted and put the water on.

"Oh, I've done all that, pues, and the Señor Professor has his hot water and he's shaving now. And I've boiled the milk and the coffee's on the fire. And I can cook the oatmeal, and eggs in many manners, and that Lola says she knows to make the little strips of bacon of pork. But we can't do eggs in water without their shells, and the Señor Professor will ask for his eggs in that mode with all certainty, and what shall we do? He is already very nervous."

I decided that the Professor had better have his eggs some

other way than poached, and I told Nieves to go and make toast. Then I shaved and dressed and went out into the patio.

The Professor, red in the face, was walking up and down with a fly swatter in one hand and a table napkin in the other, swiping at imaginary flies with both impartially. I said, "Good morning."

"My oatmeal was overcooked, and I already have indigestion," he said, dropping the swatter and killing with his hand a real fly that had just settled on his cheek. "Er—good morning. And I asked for poached eggs twelve—" he pulled out his big silver watch— "no, twelve and a half minutes ago, and they haven't come yet."

I explained about Consorcia and asked if he would mind having his eggs fried. He looked at me pityingly.

"Come here and look," he said and marched across the patio. "Here is my diet sheet, in English and Spanish, pinned up at the door of the dining room for everybody's convenience. Look! *Poached* eggs. You do understand, don't you, that the great convenience of this diet sheet is that it lists, not what I can't eat, but what I can? Surely nothing could be simpler?"

Before I could answer him, Mrs. Fountanney, in a surprisingly girlish blue kimono, emerged from the kitchen carrying a plate.

"Good morning," she said. "I hope you don't mind my going into the kitchen. Come along, Logan. Here are your poached eggs. Come and eat them before you make your indigestion worse."

The Professor meekly followed his wife and was nearly knocked down by Cayetano who came bounding into the patio.

"Señor! The lime! It has in this moment arrived. And it has come in that very big truck that usually takes melons all the way to Leon, and it can't pass the gate of the huerta, and the men say they won't carry it all the way to the shed, and they are dumping it right there in the street, and what shall we do?"

I knew this was one of those days when you want to leave Mexico within twenty-four hours, never to return. The servants, sensing an atmosphere of crisis, passed the buck of responsibility from one to the other and, rather than make the smallest decision, came running to me about everything. The pigs escaped and churned up the canna bed. The pump went wrong. Aurora dropped a big glass flower bowl she had no business with, sat down among the shards in the middle of the patio, and wept. Ten ginger ales were missing from a case that had arrived the day before, and Silvanito found the empties hidden down the huerta, where some peons had been at work, opening up new ground. I had my breakfast in the patio at about eleven, and, just at I sat down, Don Bernabé arrived with his estimates for a new bungalow. I told him to leave them with me and come back in the afternoon.

"Forgive me, señor," he said, bowing. "Forgive me if I put myself against the flow of your speech, but we should decide with urgentacy. I have been informed that the work on the new jetty is to begin with all certaintaty at once so that we should consecure the necessary masons for our own operation of construction today of one time. And there still remains much work on the house of the Señor Engineer of the Oven."

Cayetano bobbed up again.

"It is as I said, señor. Those truckers have unloaded half the lime in the street, and now they have gone to the cantina so what shall we do?"

"Of course," said Don Bernabé, "we could celebrate a contract with my son by which he would respond for bringing the needed peons and trowels on an indicated date, say, in the week that enters."

"The cooking oil has finished itself," cried Nieves from the kitchen doorway. "Do I open a big can, or a little can, or the very little one, or the other class of oil, that which you said was made of the little seeds of sesame?"

"Though even thus," said Don Bernabé, "they might get drunk, being contractated, and then they might forget and go to work on the jetty after all."

"And," said Nieves, "if that Lola doesn't at the finish and the end find any meat of beef, what shall we do about lunch? Aurora says she knows to cook artichokes because she's seen Candelaria do it, but she says she wouldn't eat them herself because of the danger, and I can always make a dry soup of rice, but there aren't any artichokes, and all the world knows to cook beans, but then the Señor Professor doesn't like them because they give him a strong air in the stomach."

"I know how to make mayonnaise," said Cayetano. "But what do we do about the lime? The agreement was for the lime to be put, and that means inside the huerta. Do I go and tell them in the cantina that we don't pay unless they throw it inside? You showed me yourself how to make mayonnaise. And Martinis."

Lola came lumbering across the patio and started talking to the others. Then they all talked at once.

"If we didn't give them any little centavos in advance," said Don Bernabé, "they wouldn't have money to inebriate themselves, but then we wouldn't have them assured, and still they might go and work on the jetty."

Just then the Professor walked slowly through the patio, and a tense hush fell. Don Bernabé put on his hat and took it off, but the Professor didn't notice and continued into the huerta. Then everybody started talking again. Lola was saying that a bull had been killed the previous night.

"So you managed to get meat for lunch?" I asked.

"Oh, no," said Lola, "no one will buy it. The meat is hanging there in the plaza, but no one will buy it although Don Vicente is giving it cheap. You see, the bull was very angry when it was killed, and the meat has come out red red, and no one would eat it, pues."

"So what do we make for lunch?" asked Nieves.

Little Silvanito came hopping into the patio.

"I have cut my foot," he said, "and that is why I go jumping. Will you cure me?"

He handed me a note from Mr. Humpel.

> Sir! One says that the cook, Consorcia, is again over-drunken and comes not, which is not to wonder, for she is an acquainted souser. I am rousing my oven, and for the

midday eating will be a Humpel pudding-pie after the English art, apples with carnations. As grease, I use an American lard, what I can eat on my bread, it is a fine lard, it is like German lard, so you need have no fear of indigesting. I am to command in my cook department. I thank you.

While I read, everyone watched in silence, apprehensive—or perhaps hopeful—of some crowning disaster. When I smiled, they all started talking again. Then Lola belched, and as the sound reverberated, a prolonged clattering came from Fordyce's room.

"What ever's that?" I asked.

"It's the señor," said Nieves, "the rare one. Every day, very early at midday, he puts himself very angry, angry like the bull they killed, and then he kicks his chamber pot across the room."

"But why?"

"Who knows," said Nieves. "He doesn't use it, but I always leave it there for the doubts. But who knows why he kicks it, pues."

The door of Fordyce's room opened, and he walked out scowling. I asked if anything were wrong.

"Damned unhygienic things," he muttered and stalked out into the huerta. "Climate's as foul as California," he called over his shoulder.

Aurora sidled up to the circle round my table.

"I put an eye to the door of the larder," she said, "and it sees itself that there are still many little cans of sardines, and we could throw a hand to these for the lunch of the Señor Profesor."

Suddenly Don Bernabé stooped to pick up his sombrero. He put it on and took it off with a wide flourish and a graceful swoop of the blood-red sarape hanging over his shoulder. I looked up. There was Doña Chabela, with a huge enamel platter piled with meat and accompanied by four children of varying sizes.

"Here I am," she said, "with all and helpers. I heard your cook hadn't arrived, so we've come to make your dinner. Look what good meat. Those of here won't buy it because they say the bull was angry. And what is he in the bull ring? The day after a bullfight there is always good fresh meat. With permission."

She made straight for the kitchen, and one by one the servants trailed after her. In a moment a hum of efficient bustle began. I told Doña Chabela with what thankfulness I would leave dinner to her, sent Cayetano to do his best about the lime, attended to Silvanito's cut, and took Don Bernabé up to the roof terrace to go into his estimates. This was a slow and complicated business, involving the working out of rectilinear and cubic measurements of foundations and walls. My own arithmetic is poor, and Don Bernabé's is positively fanciful.

There were plenty of interruptions. Silvanito came and told me that Valentina, the mother of Nieves, had come to see what offered itself to do and should she make tortillas. Then I heard Lady Connemara's voice.

"Hey," she shouted. "Told your drinking cook's not come. I'm going to make you some beaten biscuit."

There were a great many people in the kitchen already, but I was leaving that department to Doña Chabela. I had lost the thread of my calculations.

"When we have rebated the space of the doors and windows from the totality of area of wall, we must put back the space of the door we have decided not to make," said Don Bernabé helpfully.

In a few minutes I heard the chatter of voices coming up from the beach, and then a great boom of laughter rose above the chatter. Rendel and his gang were arriving, several of them carrying plates of caviar and foie gras.

I got drinks myself, and Rendel and his friends tucked into the good things they had brought.

Time went by. Lunch was already very late. The Professor didn't mention the time. He had some foie gras. Mrs. Fountanney came out of their room, greeted everybody calmly, and shot a swift glance at her husband who looked guilty. Suddenly

Cayetano emerged from under a coffee bush, with a big earthenware pot in one hand and a bottle of oil and an egg beater in the other.

"See," he said, "I have made the mayonnaise, and it didn't cut itself. It is stiff stiff, and I have made much and what shall we throw it on, pues?"

"But what about the lime?"

"The lime, señor? Oh, the men came back from the cantina and put it all in the shed, that's all."

"And what about your tables?"

He clapped his hand to his head and turned scarlet.

"The tables! I didn't remember. Now I'm in the oven. I go of one time at the run to tend them, for Doña Chabela says that dinner is ready at once right now, in half an hour."

He ran off to the kitchen, and I wondered what Doña Chabela would do with the mayonnaise.

More time went by. Three o'clock belonged to the past.

Suddenly Doña Chabela appeared. Her face was shiny, and a good many things had been spilled down her dress.

"Dinner is ready," she said. "Why don't you all stay? There's plenty, and I've told Cayetano to lay more tables."

"But won't that be an awful lot of trouble? We brought our own," said Rendel, who had eaten most of it already. "I mean, we came to help. Well, just another little one before we go in."

The dining room had an air of subdued excitement. We all sat down and waited. Then in a rush came bread, toast, tortillas plain and toasted, and a huge cauldron of soup. It was an excellent, though rich, soup of liver and cream, but I saw the Professor help himself confidently.

The four children who had been helping Doña Chabela pattered in and settled very quietly at a table in the corner.

After the soup Doña Chabela went out. There was a long wait. And then suddenly everything came at once. There was whitefish; there were steaks; there was a big stew of meat and vegetables; there was a mountain of fried potatoes; there was a huge salad; there were beans; there was an immense steaming cabbage. As far as I could see Cayetano's mayonnaise had been poured over everything except the stew. Fordyce came in, stared round coldly, sat down with his back to the room, and tapped his plate with a knife. All the servants ran round, offering everything to everybody. The Professor was saying "Oh, oh. What? This too?" And a glance at his plate showed that diets were forgotten. Fordyce asked for three more plates, and piled them all, as though afraid he mightn't get a second chance.

Rendel ate hugely, burped hugely, and laughed hugely. I had forgotten all about Lady Connemara, but in the midst of it all she reappeared.

"Here are the beaten biscuits," she announced. "I had to wait for the oven."

Aurora came limping in, carrying a very old and battered saucepan.

"This is the purée of potato that the Señor Professor has always for his stomach," she said. "I knew it would be forgotten, so I cooked the potatoes outside in the huerta on the brazier I use for my irons and I milled them myself. But who knows if they will serve, pues?"

She put the purée on the Professor's table. He eyed it for a moment in surprise; then he took three big spoonfuls.

By now there was a merry noise in the dining room. Only Fordyce was silent, his head tucked over his plates. I didn't hear Silvanito open the door, but a cloud of steam was wafted into the room, steam spicy with the scent of cloves, and there in the doorway stood Mr. Humpel with Paz a pace behind him. He was carrying a great dish on a tray and beaming. All eyes turned toward him.

"And here, my dames and gentlemen," he said, "is the apple Humpel pie."

The next day was even sultrier and more stifling. The air shimmered above the shrunken lake, and warm gusts irrupted into the house every time a door was opened. Consorcia still didn't come.

"What shall we do?" said Nieves when we had got through breakfast. "Doña Chabela used up all the meat she brought, and she used also all the vegetables that should have lasted until you go again to Guadalajara. And Don Vicente says we owe eighteen pesos sixty centavos for the meat of yesterday, and he's got nothing but scrag left. Of course Doña Chabela may come again today, but she left for Guadalajara by the six o'clock bus."

I sent Nieves to buy bones and soup meat. Mr. Humpel, apprised early of Consorcia's continued nonarrival, had sent to say that he would make a "mariners' puddingcake with corinths." We could, of course, kill a fowl, and I had canned peas and asparagus. But it would be a makeshift meal, lacking the line a good cook gives to food in the way a good conductor does to music, and we could not go on like that. It was something, it's true, that Fordyce had gone off to Guadalajara the previous evening, but on the other hand I felt certain nobody would come to help today. The novelty would have worn off, and anyway the heat was far too great. A certain amount of formless cloud haze now hung over the far end of the lake, closing down slowly over the hills and packing the hot air tighter among the tired fruit gardens and dusty lanes of the little villages along the shore.

A man walked in from the street, took off his hat, and asked very politely if I didn't want to buy a petate. I said I didn't. He went but returned in a moment with a companion, both carrying huge rolls of mats, and spread them all over the patio. They had that tender green radiance, fading into palest lemon, that new mats have. They soon turn a coarse, bright yellow, but when they are new they are as fresh as the morning.

"They are of very good reeds, from down there, by San Nicolás Ybarra," said the man.

The servants gradually gathered and began fingering the petates and asking prices.

"Much very dear," said Lola. "In Ocotlán I could get a bigger one cheaper."

"Of course you could," said the man. "But then you'd have to bring it here."

"Well, if I were down there, I'd be coming back, wouldn't I?" said Lola scornfully. "He's one of those who don't have a head," she added to Aurora, and lumbered off trailing her floor mop.

Suddenly Mrs. Fountanney appeared.

"Look," she said, "I hope you won't think I'm interfering, but I can easily manage lunch. Let me just sit there and imagine I'm you."

I protested but was very glad she insisted.

"I can see you've had about enough. Yesterday alone was sufficient to make anybody who was running a place like this put straws in his hair. I haven't much Spanish, but I do know how to cook."

I said that in that case what I would do would be to go into Chapala and find out what had happened to Consorcia. Thankfully I gave Mrs. Fountanney the keys of the stores, told her to have all the fowls killed if she wanted, and set off.

In Chapala I had no difficulty at all in finding out about Consorcia. This time everybody knew where she was. She had been locked up on Saturday night and again on Sunday night, and she was still in the prison because she couldn't pay her fine. I went along to the comisaría. Through the big barred wooden door at the end of the courtyard, I could see Consorcia sitting bolt upright on a stone bench, her arms folded. I went up and saw the judge, a tall, anemic young man sitting behind a rickety table and playing with a small bunch of flowers. He was in a deep abstraction, and I never saw anyone look more bored. His little room was mean and bare, but his expression indicated that that place for which his spirit had left it was a desert too. He returned to the real world to allow me to pay Consorcia's fine, but he only returned in part. All the time his drugged attention was mostly somewhere else, and as I left him he sank back into his dream life, fiddling with the withered nosegay.

Consorcia rose with immense dignity and came through the big barred door. Her face wore the ravaged look one sees on the face of the Madonna in an Italian *Pietà*. It had an anguished exaltation that should have been born of exhilarating tragedy, not of drink. We passed out of the comisaría through the passage where the soldiers on duty sat on stiff chairs, their collars unbuttoned and their rifles stacked in a corner.

"Hey, Consorcia," called one, jeeringly but without malice. "Qué tal?"

"Same to you, lad," said Consorcia evenly, her face a sculpture of austere nobility, "and I hope your Rita gives you horns."

Outside on the sidewalk she stopped.

"Well, come along, Consorcia, get into the car."

She gazed at the paving stones for a long moment.

"I regret, señor, it gives me much pain, but I can no longer work in your good house."

"Don't be silly, Consorcia," I said. "Let's forget all about that. Come along now, we want you to make lunch, and a cake for tea—one of your good chocolate cakes."

She did not lift her eyes.

"I cannot, señor. It is nothing that I was drunk or that they threw me into the can. That has often happened before. But I left you planted, and now you come and pay my fine, and you say, 'Come along,' as if nothing had happened. And so I have shame, and I cannot work more in your good house."

For a moment she was silent. Then she looked up at me, her fine eyes proud as dark steel, but steel with a glint in it, a glint that seemed to say, "It's a cockeyed world, and we all see it with different sorts of squint, but each of us has to follow the crooked path that looks to him straight. Isn't that so?"

"And any time you want anything bought in Chapala, just send to me. I am at your orders as your agent," she said, and, with an inclination of her bold, statuesque head, she strode away across the square.

Nobody in Chapala knew of another available cook, so, instead of returning for lunch, I drove on to Guadalajara, where I had shopping to do anyhow, and made further inquiries. None of them proved fruitful, and I started home in the late afternoon, tired and despondent. The streets were deserted, the car was like an oven, and even the open country, drab and arid under a leaden sky, matched my dismal mood. As the brown miles slid by, I hated Mexico.

"The heat's unbearable, the Indios unreliable, the price-levels incalculable, and the foreigners insufferable," I thought bitterly. "I'd do much better to quit."

From above Ixtlahuacán I looked down on the lake, lifeless and ashen between slaty hills. The clouds were building up now toward the eastern end, and a hot breeze was stirring. It was a sad prospect. Over Chapala itself hung a haze of dust through which the outlines of individual buildings loomed vague and nebulous. I began to think of Consorcia. She was an Indio; indeed, she did not look as if she had any but Indio ancestry. Yet her character was very clear cut, the very opposite of that of most Indios, which is, or in daily life seems to be, of a viscous consistency, ready to take any form. If Consorcia said she was shamed and was not coming, a blind nitwit would have known the futility of trying to make her change her mind. Usually an Indio will say, "Yes, I'll come tomorrow, that is, if God gives me license, and if the bus runs, but then it often doesn't, and if, at the finish and the end, at the last hour, I animate myself to come, who knows?" He has a horror of committing himself. His character seldom makes a clear statement; it seems to run, to clot and liquefy, like honey or like slime, according to the individual and the circumstances of the moment. It prefers a state of flux. Yet the ancestors of these Indios, and of Consorcia and Venustiano, who in his own unaggressive way is clear cut enough, do not appear to have been a wishy-washy people. Not, that is, if their sculptures are to be believed. These make very clear statements. I am cruel, says one God; I am serene, says another. I wondered whether Consorcia and Venustiano and those like them live in the true likeness of the free ancient Indios, whereas the others, who cannot describe what they have done, let alone what they wish or intend to do, without giving one the feeling that one is looking at a pointillist painting from too close at hand, are instinctively noncommittal because thus, though no praise can accrue, neither can any blame fall; and a people long held at the slave level can expect no benefit from earning praise but many stripes from getting in the way of blame. It was a depressing thought, for Consorcia and Venustiano are in a tiny minority, and Mexico is trying to become a nation of free men. But optimism, by which we must all live, suggested that Consorcia and Venustian might be a leaven, a yeast that would turn this inert, irresponsible dough into a decent, noble bread. And all the way, over the jumps and jolts of the dusty road, the engine beat the rhythm of four lines that I have loved since I was a child for their singing sumptuousness, and which probably brought me to Mexico in the first place:

Till the freed Indians in their native groves
Reap their own fruits and woo their sable loves,
Peru once more a race of kings behold
And other Mexicos be roofed with gold.

Which was not very relevant. No more relevant than the long pale finger of sunlight that was suddenly laid with didactic certainty across the snail-shell gray of the lake, filling the upper air with the promise of glory. But both were stimulating, and somehow the sound of laughter and cheerful voices that greeted me at the front door came to me as the most natural things in the world.

Just then Nieves and Cayetano came into the patio carrying plates of steaming turkey, bathed in chocolate chili sauce. I went and sat down in a corner with Mrs. Fountanney.

"I don't know what I'd do without you," I said. "Just think what would have happened to this meal if you hadn't been here. The turkey's delicious."

I think I must have betrayed my surprise, for Mrs. Fountanney gave a little chuckle.

"I expect you're wondering who taught me to cook Mexican dishes. It is good, isn't it?"

The Professor walked over and joined us. He had chocolate sauce all over his mustache and down his chin.

"I was just telling your wife," I said, "how much I'm going to miss you both when you return to Boston next month. As a matter of fact, I think I'm going to leave this place myself. It's something I've been considering for quite a time, and after these last few weeks I feel I can't cope with Mexico any longer."

"Never mind," said Mrs. Fountanney. "You'll feel differently in a day or two. Logan, dear, please wipe the sauce off your face, and go and see what's happened to the savory in the kitchen."

The Professor returned with Obdulia, the latter carrying a huge platter of crisp light fingers spread with frothing golden Chihuahua cheese, such as Candelaria used to make. I saw the fleeting smile on Mrs. Fountanney's lips, and the glance she exchanged with her husband, but I was already halfway to the kitchen door.

The buzz of conversation ceased as at the turn of a switch. Four brown faces turned toward me as I entered.

"Candelaria!"

Plump, beaming, and wearing a new rebozo with a long silk beard, Candelaria stood in the middle of the group. She started to speak at a tremendous rate.

"Ay, de mí, señor, I have been here in the village for three days with Doña Arcelia, and if I did not come to salute you earlier, it is because my cousin in Jiquilpan told me that you put yourself very angry when you were there, and now Arcelia tells me the same, and it is not to be wondered at with that Consorcia who cannot season and whom all the world knows for a bibber, and I bring you this goose, señor, to compose your anger."

There were some grains of maize on the floor, and a battered-looking goose was tethered by a strip of flannel to one of the legs of the kitchen table.

"That's very kind of you, Candelaria, and I'm very glad to have you back again. But tell me, how is Remedios?"

"Ah, señor, but she is most grave; she is in the agony; and that is why I come. You see, when she is sick, I must work to earn the centavos for her little medicines. But don't tell me, señor, that you are leaving. The Señor Professor told that Obdulia, who told Lola, who told Aurora and that Cayetano, though I should not have believed them when they told me had I myself not heard the Señor Professor say so."

"And I forgot to tell you, señor," said Nieves, "that Valentina, my mother, has heard from my brother, and he is not going to Campeche yet after all, but is to be an assistant in the cathedral in Guadalajara, so I could stay and serve you here. My brother will live in the household of the Lord Archbishop himself, or at the very least of a bishop, and perhaps you would give me permission to visit him on Sundays and at Holy Week, or from time in when."

"But now that I am here, señor," said Candelaria, "you need not fear, for I have given myself count of what lacks when I am away, and I shall throw an eye to that Obdulia, revise the trays of Nieves, and send Lola at a run to her broom. Already I have been teaching that Paz how to make potatoes in the German manner and how the bread of her señor should rise, though she is not quick to learn. Ay, señor, I shall not leave your house again."

Suddenly, she sat down on the floor, next to the goose, threw her apron over her head, and burst into tears.

"Dios de mi vida, señor," she sobbed. "Do not go away."

46.

I WAS sitting alone on the terrace; the night was hot and breathless, and so still that the flame of the match, as I lit my cigarette, did not so much as flicker; only the lightning, livid and restless, maintained a constant play all round the rim of the horizon. In spite of the curious sense of expectancy that precedes a storm, I felt, for the first time in many weeks, calm and at peace. It was a relief to have my terrace to myself once more and to be able to think my own thoughts. Cayetano appeared with decanter, ice and siphons. He mixed me a highball, meticulous precision in every gesture.

"Señor," he said, handing me the glass, "must you really go away? Why don't we close the posada; then it would be nice again, like it used to be?"

"The posada makes money, Cayetano, and without that how would you be paid?"

"The centavos don't call my attention—except sometimes. I am content to work just for my tortillas, and maybe a new shirt or a sombrero now and then. And you'll see, in a little while we'll be making money with the fruit trees and the rare vegetables we sow."

Such a simple solution, and so suited to the simple Indio way of life! How complex an affair we have made of our own existence, I thought, when each extra comfort becomes an extra care, and when so plain and fundamental a point of view as Cayetano's can provoke no further reaction than a smile of tolerance or derision. Yet how restful are the Indios in their simplicity, in an existence that knows nothing of the boredom of plenty, the confusion of variety, or the dreariness of persistent wit.

Across the lake, a more than usually vivid lightning flash was followed by the first growls of thunder so that I did not hear the silent figure approaching up the terrace steps until he was at my elbow.

"Good evening. May I pass?"

It was Venustiano. He strode by me, threw his sarape on the tiled floor and sat on it.

"I've come to return this," he said, indicating an old Flit gun I had lent him when he was ill in bed. "The flies didn't mind the liquid my wife bought in the village, but the little pump has served for spraying the mixture of Bordeaux on my trees. Many thanks. And what is this that all the fools are saying of you in the village?"

"What are they saying?"

"That you're going away, pues."

No curiosity or surprise could betray Venustiano's exquisite manners when I told him I planned to go to Europe; nevertheless, he managed to convey the expression of his disapproval with every civil word he uttered.

"Ah, yes," he said, "I have read that it is a fine place, and the people rich and wise. Of course, Mexico is poor, and then we have little revolutions, too, one day with another."

He fell silent, his impassive features a screen before his mind as he listened to the first heavy raindrops rattling on the banana leaves. As we watched, the wind came leaping across the huerta in sudden gusty flurries, bending the fruit trees and snapping off the sere, brittle plants at their roots. There was a crash of thunder, and Silvanito bounded up the steps onto the terrace.

"Good evening, señor. How good that you are back."

He hadn't noticed that I was not alone, and he had something to say that he didn't want the others to hear. He shuffled his feet, took off his sombrero, picked up the badger from the basket where it lay curled up with Tippet, tucked it in his sarape, and dropped two letters that he was carrying.

"Well, Silvanito?"

Monk, who considers anything that falls from above as manna expressly devised for her chewing pleasure, sprang from her chair, but Cayetano was too quick for her. He handed me the letters, one of which was registered and bore a New York postmark.

"When did this come, Silvanito? It's covered with earth."

Silvanito blushed crimson and started to chew the black ribbon of his sombrero.

"That one, pues," he said, "is the one that is not from the Señor of the Oven, who gave me the other one just now."

"Maybe, but when did the registered one come?"

"Pues," said Silvanito.

"Well?"

"It would give me much shame to tell you, señor."

"But I want to know."

"You see, it was the fault of the seeds, señor. I was sowing the seeds of radish when that Joaquín, he of the post office, came with it, and I signed the little paper myself, with all my three names, in the manner that you have taught me."

"But that must have been at least a week ago. The seeds are already sprouting."

"Little seeds of radish," said Silvanito, dropping the badger on top of Tippet in her basket, "are born very quickly."

"Letters are usually registered because they are important. Why didn't you bring it to me at once?"

"I was going to, señor, but then I remembered how you have told me very often to finish one job at a time, so I went on with the seeds, pues. I put some sticks in the ground at the end of each row and collocated the little packets on them to indicate what grew, and then I threw a hand to chasing the sow, who was in the asparagus bed, and only just now I found the empty packet of little radishes in my pocket, and I remembered the letter and went at a run to the seeds, and there it was on the little stick, so I put the packet there instead to show there were radishes, and the letter I brought to you at once, pues."

"Silvanito, you're a very careless boy," I said slitting open the envelope. "It's lucky you remembered before the rain came, for much might depend on it."

And so it did. Attached to my agents' letter was a check. *Village in the Sun* had been accepted for publication.

Well, with any luck, here was the key to the whole problem, the fare for my trip to Europe, the price of months of travel, fresh scenes, and new experiences to write about. But then again, here too were Candelaria's market lists, Cayetano's wages, a new wall for the huerta, and, best of all, that precious freedom, unknown to innkeepers, to call my soul my own.

As I gazed out across the lake, weighing the alternatives, the full fury of the storm burst upon us with all the traditional violence that accompanies the first rains in the Tropics. The water fell like a curtain, vaguely opalescent in the lightning flashes, hiding huerta, lake, and sky behind an impenetrable film. Off the roof it poured in torrents, each row of tiles discharging a miniature Niagara, beating down the blossoms and tearing off the leaves of the geraniums in the flower bed below, and throwing up its own haze of cool mist, which, drifting gently into the terrace, covered the outer paving with a sheen of tiny drops. The continuous crashing of thunder drowned all attempt at speech, and in the unceasing shimmer of the lightning the terrace scene flickered like an early one-reel movie. Venustiano gazed through the rain, gauging, no doubt, the quantity of the fall, assessing possible damage, considering tomorrow's cultivation. His wrinkled coppery face in its halo of white hair was calm and reflective. Of Silvanito I could see little, swathed as he was in the shapeless huddle of his sarape, but between the growls of the thunder I could hear the quickened tempo of his breathing as he crossed himself, and in the glare of the incessant flashes of lightning I could clearly discern the gleam of Cayetano's teeth, brilliant white against his mahogany skin.

Here is Mexico, I thought, the old and the young, standing at the gateway of the seasons, those twin aspects, so sharply contrasted, of her strangely diverse nature; Mexico parched and lush, Mexico weary and vigorous; the ancient Mexico, calm and dignified and traditional; the new generation, carefree, vital, and eager; Mexico of the subtle halftones and stately manners; Mexico, vivid and mercurial, incalculable and of infinite variety.

Gradually the violence of the downpour abated, and my three companions got up to take their leave.

Cayetano took my hand and kissed it.

"Good night, señor," he said. "May you dream with the angels."

"Good night," said Silvanito. "And I was wondering, señor, whether you will still be angry with me on the day past tomorrow, for that is the day when I complete sixteen years."

Venustiano said, "I was reading about Europe in the paper the other day, in the column called cocktail chats, and the writer seemed not to like a person he calls Pepe Stalin. This Pepe seems to have a lot and wants more. Pues, as they say, the next man's plate is always fuller."

I was alone again on my terrace. By now the arroyo was rushing in full spate, and the clatter of the stones and the surge of the water formed part of a whole orchestra of little noises—new and busy sounds whose murmur spread through the night in a gentle crescendo, like the ripple of good news across an anxious multitude. Somewhere in the village a burro brayed in hysterical pleasure, and an eager chorus of dogs took up the cry, while up from the lake shore came the voices of fishermen raised in song as they pushed out their boat for the first catch of the rainy season, the mellow notes rising clear and sweet above the bloated warbling of the bullfrogs. The very earth itself gasped and sighed thirstily as it sucked in the moisture, and the rustlings of innumerable insects, stirred to new activity, rose through the darkness in a faint and continuous whisper like the bubbles in a glass of champagne. And with the tiny sounds came all those gusts of perfume set free by the rain, the heavy aroma of tangerine blossom and of jasmine, the sharp tang of the farmyard and the subtle, heady scent of the damp earth itself. Presently, through the scattered clouds, the moon reached out an arm of pallid light over the lake shore and painted jet shadows beneath the willows, somber patches through which the first fireflies soared and twinkled. And suddenly I noticed Mr. Humpel's letter lying on the table beside me. I had forgotten all about it.

> Sir! Honored Host! I write to advise that the good Merced is hurrying all and that by the end of current month (June) I take my bride to our new home. It makes me leaving-sorrow, for I am the endurance guest in your fine boardhouse, but every bird must have its own place, though some, like my angered Gustele, lead a nestless life.
>
> Tomorrow, I send you "Prosit" and a piece of wedding pie, of my own baking. Na, had I but the fruits of the North, I make Apfelstrudel and Erdbeertorte and many good Arts of sugar-bakery. But here in Mexico, where I am three and sixty years, the air is poison and the water is poison and the people is thief and the fruits are all shine and no taste.
>
> The news of your departure comes with shocks. But when one is sick with the interior, now it is the foot, now it is the neighbor, but always it is Mexico and one is in a bad mud each day. Perhaps you make a Europe journey, where you will enjoy, but when you come back again to Vera Cruz, you strike your foot on the good earth, and the Mexican dust rises, and you make a great sneeze, and you say: "This is my Home." I thank you.
>
> HEINRICH JOACHIM HUMPEL.
> Ingeniero.

I put the letter down and a sudden gust of wind carried it out into the huerta. Kind and muddled old man! With all his Teutonic love of precision, his contempt for Mexican standards of life and conduct, he yet knew himself powerless to tear himself away from this country of his adoption. The Mexican dust, he had said. Mexican dust, pungent, irritant and subtle; only those who savor it know anything of the soul of Mexico. Now, with the rains, I thought, it is once again rich soil, ready to renew the land in all the splendor of greenery and bright flowers that for the next half year will make a garden of the whole countryside—a scene gay and transitory as the tourist life it sustains, that life, alien and superficial, with which I had in vain tried to identify myself. Well, no more of that. Six months more, and the flowers and the greenery will be swept back into the dry brown dust of Mexico, and with them will go the tourists. But the nopal and the maguey, tough and enduring, part and parcel as they are of the body of Mexico, these will remain. So too will the mango and the Indian laurel, dark and deep rooted, bowing to no seasons and, in the hot, sere landscape of May, standing even prouder and more assertive than among the lush October green; while the eucalyptus, itself a foreigner, has also found its way to the deep springs of life below the parched topsoil, and has established here a new and lasting home. And I knew now that I too must remain, must clear the weeds out of my life, and give my own roots a chance to strike deeper into the life of this land and to draw fresh vitality from the infinite variety of its moods and the rich, incalculable character of its people. Yes, Mr. Humpel, I thought, this is the home to which I shall always return.

As I rose from my chair to go indoors, a little breeze ruffled the ferns along the edge of the terrace and brought to my ears again, faint but clear, the voices of the fishermen as they pulled out across the silvery water. And the song that they sang was a song, old but never outdated, that same song which had welcomed me when first, years ago, I had come to Ajijic, a song, timeless, vague, and hopeful as the spirit of the land itself.

One day with another
The luck will surely change. . . .

San Antonio Tlayacapán,
vía Chapala,
Jalisco, México
May 30, 1949